Elephant Brain

Elephant Brain

a collection

Amar A. Abro

Elephant Brain

Hardcover ISBN: 978-1-7373559-0-8
Paperback ISBN: 978-1-7373559-1-5
Ebook ISBN: 978-1-7373559-2-2

Library of Congress Number: 2021914281

Edited By Kimberly Peticolas
Cover Design By Rachel Greenberg
Layout By Kimberly Peticolas

for you.

Stories

the quantum leaps

There they were, in this unfamiliar place, the two lovers. They felt so much confusion as they tried to take it all in. Their surroundings were felt and not perceived. They felt as if they were holding each other, warming each other with their embrace, although no sense of touch was really present. They both wondered, were they really together? *Yes, yes, for certain we are together,* they both thought.

Here she is with me, he thought.

And here he is, with me, she thought.

This new place was becoming eerily familiar. Very slowly. Something must have happened. Something to make everything so different. But what? The confusion mixed with a calming peace that began to settle over them. They continued to wonder . . . what happened?

"You died," a voice called out to them as if it was reading their thoughts. A strong sense of emotion ran through them. It was not fear, though. Neither of them felt afraid, though they felt as if they should. They felt more confused as to why these words did not make them afraid than anything else. They tried to turn and see where the voice came from. Who was this person who just told them this outrageous thing? But they realized that there was no one there. In fact, there was nothing. There was not even each other. At least not in any sense that they could see. There was no physical existence at all they realized. But that voice came from a presence that they both felt was there, all around them. For certain someone was there! Someone familiar.

"Who are you?" the man called out to nowhere.

"What do you mean, we died?" asked the woman.

"Can you not tell?" The voice replied in a calming tone. "Give it a moment. It always takes a moment."

"If we are dead," the woman said in a slow voice that led to a pause, "then you . . . you are God?"

"Yes," the voice called back in the most loving way, "I am God. And yes, you died. And now you are full of questions. Remain calm, my children, all will be explained to you in time. This is a special meeting for us. I am happy to have you both with me, together."

The presence of God surrounded the two and filled them with a euphoria that they never had remembered feeling before.

The woman continued to speak, "Where are we, why can't I recognize him, how did we die . . . ?"

"Is this Heaven? Or Hell? Or what? And what about our friends and family? Where are they? I don't understand." The man spoke his thoughts, not knowing where to begin.

God took a moment for the two lovers to feel at ease once again, and then he spoke, "My children, you are with me now, and you have nothing to fear. Trust in me, that all is as it is meant to be. Heaven? The kingdom of Heaven lies within man. This place is neither Heaven nor Hell. It is my place. The place where my beings come each time their existence ceases in each place that I send them. I do not always come to my beings after each time they die. Sometimes there is no need. But this time, you two died together, so you are here in this place together, at the same moment. This does not happen very often, so I had to come see you on this special occasion."

"This time?" asked the man. "You mean we have died before?"

"Oh yes, my child. Many times. And you will die many more."

"Many?" asked the woman. "How many? I do not remember any times before."

God laughed before answering, "I would say an infinite number of times, but you could not comprehend the idea of eternity, no matter how hard you try. It is one of the faults I purposely gave to you. You have been born many times, and you have died many times. You have been created many times, and you have ceased to exist in that created way many times. This cycle has always existed, and it always will. From stardust to form. And from form back to stardust. Always a part of my universe."

"So the Hindus were right. Reincarnation is the way of life?" the man asked God. "We go back to earth each time as someone different?"

"All religions get some of it right and some of it wrong," God told them. "What they got right is that your existence is eternal. Not just forever going forward but before as well. There is no beginning and there is no end." God brightened their surroundings with light. "Pay close attention because here is the part that you always love every time I have told you this story . . .

"You, my children, are a part of my energy, as are all things. I have created you as I have created all things. Near and far, large and small, bright and dark. All things. You are all made of the same energy that exists, and has always existed, and always will exist. You change form from time to time. You call it dying. I never liked that you chose to use that word. It is so dark. So permanent. I like to see it as transforming. You were both students of science this time around, so maybe it will suit you better if I call it a quantum leap into another existence. The quantum matter of your energy leaves your familiar place and goes on to another place. Each time you leap, you come here, to this place, for some time. My place. Sometimes we chat, sometimes we don't, and then I send you on your way to exist in another way. Each time you grow, in emotion, that is. Each time you gain more and more, and mature your beautiful souls.

And if you stay with me here long enough, all of which you have acquired before will slowly come back to you. But you cannot take it consciously with you into the next life. But fear not, my children, those experiences which you gain will never leave you. It will always be there inside of you, a part of your energy forever. Always visible when you are here, in my place, with me. Hiding inside your soul, leading you with me as the guide. You don't even realize it, but I am always there, as I am there within all things. I am what connects you with every single thing I have ever created.

You asked me why you couldn't recognize each other when you first arrived here. Can you see each other now? You were looking for an image that you have been used to seeing for the past number of years, and that image is not here. Do you understand? That image was just the form your energy took for the briefest of moments during its eternal existence. This is who you really are. Here. Now. This ball of energy is your true self. Your soul . . . My soul. The beautiful soul I created in my own image. You cannot see this image; you can only experience it. Just as love cannot be drawn on a piece of paper, existence cannot be described with an image. And you asked me how you died. Now that you are understanding, I believe this question no longer matters to you, does it? Although, as I told you, this part is important: you died together this time."

"This time?" asked the man. "We died together this time? Does that mean that in our previous lives, we knew each other as well? Have we met in our other lives before this time? Has the man I might have been before met the women that she was once? Did we find each other before?"

"My son," God began slowly, pausing to be sure the lovers were ready to hear what he had to say, "you have always found each other. When I created you, I made you both perfect in every way. Two perfect beings, perfect souls, complete. But immediately, I took some away from both of you. And I put that energy into each other. Two almost perfect beings that can only be complete when their souls come together again. It has been this way since your creation. Two fires born of the same flame. This is why you call each other soulmates.

"But you have not always been a man. And you not always a woman. My creations are vast, and all are made up of my energy. Each transformation of energy can take on any form of matter, for any period of existence . . . time, as you call it. You will want to ask me how long it will take to find each other in each existence. But you must understand. Time is not real. As I have told you, existence is eternal. If I tell you that it may have taken one billion years to find each other, you may be distressed at the thought of being apart for too long. But fear not, for one billion years does not matter in eternity. Time does not matter. There is only existence. Time is not the question that you wish to ask of me.

The question that you seek the answer to is far greater than time. It is far greater than anything. Each time you leave this place, you go on to a new existence, apart from each other. Your new consciousness exists out there, unaware of that other energy that will make you feel complete again. You go on existing in my place. And that part of you, the part I told you that lives inside you, hiding deep inside without you even realizing it with all the knowledge and emotion and experience that you have gained in all your existence, it drives you toward that other half of you. That half that I put in that other soul. And each loving moment you encounter with all other energy stays with you forever. That is why you are drawn to some people and some places and some beings without ever realizing why. It is because you have loved each other once before, and that energy hiding in that soul recognizes that loving energy in another, and it leaps for joy for being reunited with this energy that it loved once before."

The lovers felt emotions more overpowering than they had ever felt before. God stopped speaking for a moment as their energy began to brighten. It was happening. They were remembering. It was all coming back to them. So much joy was lifting them both. They were having visions of their experiences, not just in the life that they had just left, but in all the times that they had existed before. Together.

"We always find each other," the woman said. "If even for brief moments in each existence, we always find each other." She was so overcome with joy that she could no longer speak. She embraced her lover as he embraced her back.

The man managed to say the only thing he knew was left to say. "Yes. Yes, it is all familiar now. We understand. The reason for this. For all of this. Thank you, God. Thank you again for it. We know the answer to the question that we were meant to ask you.

"Love," spoke God. "Love is the answer. You find each other every time because of love. It is why I created the heavens and the earth. It is the purpose of all existence. All roads lead back to love, my children. And now I will tell you of some of those times when you found each other before, as you always ask me to do . . . Six thousand years ago, a man was pulling a rope that was dragging a stone to build a pyramid for the Pharaoh when he caught the eyes of a woman who poured him a cup of water, and his heart leaped with joy. His soul recognized her soul. You were that man, and you were that woman.

"Six hundred years ago, a man was boarding a ship that was to cross the ocean for the first time, and as he boarded that ship never to return, he kissed his lifelong lover goodbye, and both of their hearts sank to the bottom of the ocean. You were that man, and you were that woman.

"Sixty billion years ago, thirty-two million lightyears from earth, in the constellation Pisces, there was a star. Orbiting that star was a planet with a beautifully brilliant moon. That sun warmed that moon and shined her light on his glorious surface. And they shared the most loving of energies for billions of years. You were that sun. And you were that moon.

"And some place out there some years ago in a mountainous land, there was a wolf that took a swim in a lake. And as he entered the water, he felt an emotion of joy that warmed his heart. As if he was meant to get lost in the embracing water. You were that wolf, and you were that lake.

"And in that same mountain, there once was a woman who sat alone beneath a magnificent oak tree in a field surrounded by flowers and valleys. And as the wind blew through her hair, she felt so loved that she shed a tear of joy. You were that woman, and you were that tree.

"And finally, one day many years from now, two beings of energy whom I have created will have experienced all that I need them to experience. They will have grown and matured until they can grow and mature no more. They will come together and become a single soul, filled with the brightest of lights and the warmest love. Complete and inseparable. One soul. One love. So that they may stay here, in this place, with me. Forever. And you will be that soul."

the cave

"Why does it hurt so much?"

Her heart. It was filled with pain. She kept asking herself this question. She even foolishly hoped for an answer. *From where? From whom? Who knows.* She thought she knew the answer, and she was afraid of it. She was afraid of what this meant for her future. Afraid of what she was going to do.

"This pain is too much. I cannot go on this way."

So she devised a plan. A plan that would end her heartaches. She would stop feeling. She would lock her heart away. This was the answer.

"How can my heart ache if I have no heart to soothe?" She laughed at herself out of cynicism, but she knew her laughs were to mask the sadness of what she truly did not desire to do. *But I must do it anyway*, she thought. The pain is too great.

So she set out to find a cave. A deep, dark, daunting cave. A cave where no light could exist. A cave that would be the perfect place to hide away her broken heart. A place where no one would find it. No one would ever go after it even if they knew it was there. She searched and searched until she found just the right cave. As she walked into it, all alone and with only her sadness to comfort her, she cried. This is not how it was supposed to go. She did not truly want to lock her heart away. She knew deep down that she was truly at her happiest when her heart was full of love. How could she not have been? The feelings of love are too great to be explained with words. But she kept on, step after step, farther and farther into the black cave. There was no turning back. She had made up her mind. This was the only way to take away the pain. She must stop feeling altogether. She must die on the inside.

Finally, she had reached the end of the cave. She felt as if she had been walking forever. But there it was, the deepest and darkest expanse of the most daunting and uninviting of caves. She stopped there and took a deep breath. *This is just the place*, she thought to herself. *No one will come here. No one would dare risk entering this place to come near my heart again.* And so she decided that that was the place where she would leave her heart. Hidden away. Safe from the outside world.

But it wasn't enough to just set it there. No. In the small chance that someone would be daring enough to go looking for it, they might find it. She must protect it even more. She must bury it into the earth. She dropped to the ground, and she began to dig. Using her bare hands and the grit of her nails, she would dig a hole. A hole that no one would ever find. She used her hands to pry away the rock beneath her feet, using all of her might until she was satisfied that the place was beyond the reach of anyone who would ever attempt to find her heart again.

And once again, she closed her eyes and took a deep breath. The tears made their way down her face, one by one. First, one drop down her right cheek, and then one down her left. And then she did it. She took it from her chest, and she laid her heart down on the bed of the earth that was at the bottom of the hole. She kneeled over it, still with her eyes closed. The teardrops continued to fall. They fell from her cheeks down onto the heart that now lay lonely beneath her.

"My own teardrops will be the last bit of comfort my heart will ever feel."

This is not what she wanted. This is not how it was supposed to be.

The earth moved through her fingers as her hands swept to fill the shadowy hole. She reached for the biggest of boulders that she could manage to move. She pulled and she pushed and she covered the hole, ensuring that her heart would never escape that place. And when she cried her last tear and took her last deep breath, she stood and turned and began to make her way out.

The cave seemed even darker than she remembered it to be on her journey in. *Maybe everything will be darker in the world to me now, too,* she thought to herself as she moved with no heart. Her tears had stopped, and her mind was struggling to be at ease as she moved to exit the cave.

"It's so dark," she kept saying. "If only that light up ahead was just a bit brighter, I could find my way out of this sad place."

Her steps came with great struggles as she was troubled by the darkness trying to walk out of the cave. Ahead of her, near the far end, was a fragment of light. It looked like a star, sparkling in the night sky. Bright and majestic, but too small and too far in the distance to show her the way.

"If only that light would help me to see."

She stopped in her tracks as a thought came to her mind. On her long journey into the cave, there was no light. There was only darkness and void in the haunting abyss. So where was this light coming from? *Did someone follow me here? Would someone be brave enough to come to this place after me and my heart? Surely not! But then what was this light?*

"Hello!" she cried out, her voice echoing up the walls and traveling through the dark cave. She stood silent and listened in the darkness, hoping for an answer to come back. But there was nothing. Only silence. So she called out again, her eyes squinting at the distant light, secretly wishing to hear a voice call back to her. But again, there was nothing. Her sadness remained. She began to move forward once again. She felt foolish thinking that someone would be there for her. "No one would come for my heart in this cave."

As she stopped once more, she turned her head back and looked toward the end of the cave, down to the place where she had left her heart. "Goodbye," she whispered sadly in a warm breath. As she began with her first step to finally exit, she slowly turned her head back and froze in her place. The light. It brightened. She became confused and frightened and stood still in the darkness. The light seemed to have life.

"How can this be?"

It flickered and breathed as if it had a pulse, floating there in the distance for moments before beginning to move. And then the light came hurtling at her, getting bigger and brighter as it moved quickly through the cool air. She just stood there. What else could she do? There was nowhere to run. No refuge to be found.

The brightness of the light became bolder and louder. It became too much for her eyes. She looked on, squinting, holding her arm up for cover as the light fell upon her face. It was a sudden explosion of brilliance that engulfed and warmed her. In a moment, she stood there, letting her arm down slowly, turning her head all about her. There was no speck of light anymore; there was only brightness. Illumination all around her. She stood in her place and turned her head with confusion. Light stretched in every direction with a bright and warming white hue. The walls of the cave were gone. There was nothing. Only light remained. Then, strangely, the fear that she had first felt was gone. It had quickly subsided. She felt safe and at ease in this place, even with all of her confusion.

One more time she called out, "Hello?" But this time with a smile on her face and a calm peace in her voice.

"Hello," replied a voice. She turned her head thinking the voice had called out from behind her; but again, only brightness was there. She turned again, quickly, in every direction, looking left and right and up and down in wonder all around her. There was no one to be seen. "I am here," the voice gently called. And with those words, she felt an embrace. She stopped looking about her, knowing she would find no one, but not afraid of this realization.

"Who are you?" she asked, as she felt a comforting warmth from the light.

And in the most beautiful way that the woman had ever imagined, the voice answered, "I am God."

A strange thought occurred to her upon hearing God's reply. It was not a question of how it could be that she was talking with God. But instead, how she could be so accepting of this to be true. She felt no need to question the reality. No feeling of being lied to or led astray. She knew the reply was truth. She was certain that she was in the true presence of God, and so she moved on from that point. "Where are we now?" she asked out to God. "What is this place?"

"We are in the cave, my child. The cave that you entered to abandon your heart."

"But how? This is surely not the same place where I just was. The walls of jagged rock and the darkness and the cold abyss? The cave that frightened me and was so unwelcoming and caused me such fear. It cannot be this place."

"My child," God replied to her, "in my presence, there is no fear. There is no darkness, and there is no sorrow. When we are together, we are the light of the world. When we are together, there is only peace."

"What are you doing here? Why have you come to me?" she continued to God with a harsher tone in her voice. She realized that God may have shown up to thwart her plan, and this was not okay. It was her decision to make. It was her heart to let go. "I came here to end my pain and to bury my heart. Surely, you already know. I was on my way out, and you came and stopped me. I do not need your assistance. Let me be on my way."

"Yes, I know why you are here, my child." God spoke softly and slowly as she stubbornly listened to the words. "I am sorry for your pain. It is my pain as well. Every time one of you suffers, I suffer the same. This time your pain is severe. What happened was not easy. I am sorry that you must suffer, but I am here to be with you. I know it is back there. Your heart. Buried as far away in a place that you could ever imagine, so that no one would find it again. You must understand that I understand why you chose to do this. And if you realize that to be true, you will know why I am here."

"You want me to go back for it, don't you?" she spoke with a rasp in her voice, upset that God had come to foil her plan. "Well, I won't. It is my decision, God. I am sorry that it saddens you, but it is my burden to carry. Maybe you do understand, and you know how I feel. But if that is true, how can you ask me to go back for it? The pain is too great, and I would rather live empty than to live in the darkness. Choice. And free will. That is a gift you gave to us, right? Then let this be my decision."

"Free will indeed, my child. I only intervene when called upon."

"Well then, you can go and leave me on my way. I never called out to you. I did not ask for your help."

God let out a gentle laugh as the words began with a reply, "You did not ask for my help, you say? My child, your lips and your ears may be what you think lead you now, but do not be foolish. These are not who you really are. These are not parts of your soul. No, it is something much greater that is truly you. Something you brought here to bury and abandon. Your heart, my child. Your heart has been screaming for me for all time. You are blinded by your pain, and right now you cannot see the truth. You can never escape from your heart. You can bury it deep down in a cave and walk away from it as far as you please, but it will remain a part of you forever. That part of you—that is me."

The woman became upset, and the frustration grew in her voice. "If my heart has been screaming for you, then where have you been? Why let me suffer for so long and come to me now? You have forsaken me, and now you want me to accept you and follow your commands?" Tears came back to her eyes as she cried out these words, "Why, God? Why would I do such things now? Why did you create me if you would allow me to feel such sorrow?!" She sobbed out loud as she fell to the ground. She buried her face in her arms and felt every emotion imaginable, all rushing through her at once. Then she felt a warming embrace that lifted her up, and she opened her eyes to the brightness all around her once more.

"My child, I did not create you," God spoke with love in his voice. "My child, I *am* you."

"You are me?" she struggled to ask.

"I have come to you this time because this is when you need me the most. I am offering you knowledge so that you can live on the right path. If you will follow me, just for a bit, I would like to show you something. I will make you a deal, my child. I give you my word. If you give me this chance to show you the meaning, I will leave you with your decision. I will assure you that your heart can remain buried there for as long as you wish. I will protect this cave so that no one will ever come near it. And you can go on living that way for as long as you please."

The woman bowed her head and spent a moment in thought. *What a deal God has offered me.* Surely, she could give God a few more moments of her time in exchange for this service.

"Yes," she replied, "I will follow you. Show me what you intend to show me, God, and then let me make my decision."

The brightness of the light all around her intensified

with great magnitude. The feeling of God comforted her as she came to a place of peace and harmony. "You see, my child, I often hear the cries of my children calling out this same question: 'Why did you create me?' I hear it again and again. But you must understand your true origins in a new way. I did not create you. For if I had created you, you would not be a part of me. Look, all around you now. The cosmos. This place. Your existence. I did not create it out of me.

"No. The truth is that all of it is me. I am every single part of every single thing there is and ever was. Including you. It is all a collection. A breakdown of bits and pieces of all the same things. Even there, the void, where you think there is nothing, is still the existence of me. You see, everything is connected. Everything is from the same dust. And you are a part of this existence. Capable of becoming everything that there ever was. You always have been, just in different ways. You were not created as the sole being that you think that you are, but instead you are the extension of me."

She looked all about her as God took her through the new place. Everything she had ever known was there in front of her. All the familiar places. There they were, in front of her. All the familiar people, their faces passing by. All the familiar things, some living and some unconscious. Some grand, and some small. And then the unfamiliar places. Some near and some far. Some far away galaxies and some exotic paradises. Existence, all of it, was being paraded before her eyes.

God continued to speak as she looked on with

marvel, "All of this, you see, is me. It is all a great summation of energy. I have spread myself vast over a great period of time. All of it matters. All of it has worth. All of it is important to me. Especially this."

The visions before her spun into a blur as an object appeared before her. She walked toward what God was leading her to see. It was an object that was turned to face away from her. So, she moved slowly to walk around it to see what it was. A mirror. She looked into it to see herself standing there, staring back at her own image. She locked eyes with herself and fell into a gaze. She moved closer to see her own irises as the colors in her eyes seemed so bright and so bold. The image of the entire universe lay there before her. All mighty and magnificent. She couldn't look away as she listened to God's voice continue.

"You see, you have been created in my image. You are a part of me. Your existence is vast and eternal. This life that you are in now is just a fragment of the time you are spending away from being a part of me." As she looked into her own eyes in the mirror, the image of the universe in her transformed slowly, and it faded into an image of her standing there, alone in the mirror. She saw what God wanted her to see—an image of the universe, in all of its glory, and the creation of herself as a part of it. A piece of the great existence taken out and made into her.

"But why?" she cried out to God as she reached forward with her hand. The mirror faded away, and she found herself among the stars, looking with wonder at the amazing creation of existence in every direction. "Why, God, did you take a part of yourself and give it to me? Why did you not stay the great whole self that you used to be?" Again, a sadness came in her voice, "I am not worthy to exist as a part taken from you."

God went on thought there was sorrow in the woman's voice. "When you buried your heart back there, in that sad and dark place, what did you feel?"

She stood silent for a moment, and she lowered her head. "Sadness," she answered, "darkness, and emptiness. A feeling of void that I feared could never be filled."

"And what, my child, went missing from you that made you feel that way?"

Tears of sadness returned to her eyes as she thought of the answer so quickly and so sure. "Love, my God. Love went missing from my heart, and it made me feel that way."

"And now I have come to you. This great journey I have led you on. And you ask me this question. This question of why. You ask me why. Why did I give you a life from me? Why did I not stay whole as God and remain with all energy and existence? This is the greatest of questions that can ever be answered. Together, here in my place, I have shown you great things so that you may not need to question again. The answer is within you, my child. So answer me, if you will."

"Love, my God. Love is the answer," she replied with great emotion in her voice. "You did it for love."

"Yes, my child. I did it for love. You see, for all this great existence, the endless space of the cosmos, it is all me, just as I said. And as I am the creator, if I am to exist, then even I must have a purpose. And that purpose is love. For all the energy that I have ever created will twist and turn. It will expand and it will convert. Just as I said, all energy will change many times. And it will take a great time until it finds its true destiny. Its destiny to become love. Only then can it finally end its long journey and remain a part of me once again, forever."

God paused a long moment before speaking again. "So, I ask that you remain with your heart. Because you see, my child, love always wins in the end."

Her emotions ran wild as God's words turned into visions. She knew it to be true. The words that she heard were what she had known all along. She felt a lump in her throat as she struggled to speak. "What if that is a lie?" she slowly asked God with her last attempt at rebuttal.

"Then it is the greatest lie that has ever been told." The words came with power as God continued to speak. "Faith, my child. When you think love has failed, then you are not looking ahead. For if love has not yet conquered, then this is not yet the end. I will never subject you to anything that you cannot handle. This existence has been here in the past far before you could ever imagine. And it will continue and move forward for a great time to come. There is an end to this. To all of this. This great existence. This era that you have come to know. These billions of years and these far-reaching cosmos. There will be an end to all of it. It will take a great amount of time, but time is something that I have. That end will be in glory when all of the energy in all of existence has learned to become what it was created to become. All of the universe will exist in a never-ending peace, and a harmony when this time will finally come. That time, my child, will come when all of existence has evolved to become love."

The woman remained silent as she felt the words of God tremble all throughout her. She dared not question them again, for she felt their sincere truth. "And now I must decide," she spoke on to God, "if I want to return to my heart or go on alone?"

"Yes. The decision is always yours. I know the pain and the sorrow are hard, but you always have a choice. But remember, my child, I did not bring you this far to abandon you now."

"But the darkness," she replied, "I am afraid of its return. When you came to me in the cave, your light showed me the way. How can I call you to return to me if the light has faded again?"

"My child," God spoke in a solemn voice, "don't you see? I told you, there in the cave— together, we are the light of the world. Faith, my child. You will never need to fear."

"Yes," she replied, "but how do I call you again? How do I summon you to my side?"

"Look closer at your heart, my loving child," God's

voice rang out with love. "The light is everywhere. I am always at your side . . . We are always together."

Tears of joy ran down her cheeks as she gently put her hands upon her face. She had made up her mind. She floated from the heavens back down to the place where she had buried her heart. The cave was no more, though. The dark walls were all gone, and the dark abyss was now bright. All that remained was a boulder covering the hole where she left the part of herself that God cared for so much. She stood there and watched as the boulder vanished away. The brightest and most beautiful of lights floated before her as she broke out in a smile. She said to herself, "Love will win in the end, I will always have faith."

the machine

He didn't know where he was going. He didn't know why he was going there. He just walked. Aimlessly and without purpose. Through the darkness of the night desert air, he walked. Guided by the vastness of the sky, he walked. There were many others, heavy-hearted, like him. *But surely*, he thought to himself, *none of them can understand my struggle. None of them are hurting like I am.*

His journey began a long time ago. Or maybe it was recently. He couldn't tell anymore. *Change the world.* That is what he was asked to do. So hopeful back then. So full of courage and so many dreams in his eyes. But those days seemed like a lifetime ago now. His joy had been replaced with pain, and his inspirations had been overshadowed by sorrow. He felt pain in his heart. He yearned for his heart's desires, but they were always kept away from him. So, he begged, and he bargained with his eyes closed and his head down, but it wouldn't come. He looked to the sky day after day and night after night searching for an answer. But it was always the same. Nothing. He could not understand why his life had turned out this way. He felt that he was a righteous man and that he had lived an upright life. There had never been a time that he did not put others before himself. He was truly altruistic. There was never a time that he did not offer himself for the sake of another; yet in his darkest times, he felt so alone. Where was the world when he needed it? He gazed at the sky to find his way by the stars as his father had taught him to do. "When you are lost, the stars will guide you," his father had said. "When you cannot find the way, the stars will shine." The stars became his most detailed map. They had helped him to cross the great desert for many years. Always the same magnificent wonder of shimmering lights and marvelous galaxies that were worlds away. He could always rely on the stars. They were always there for him. He found comfort in their reliability. One night, when his father was teaching him to navigate by the celestial bodies, he pointed to one star that shone brighter than all the ones around it. "Do you see that, my son?" his father said as he pointed to the glistening diamond in the sky. "That is your star."

"My star?"

"Yes, my son, that is your star. You are a warrior of light. Never forget that. And when you have lost your way, find that star, for it will guide you along the right path."

Over the many years since that day, the man had learned to find his star a moment after gazing upon the night sky. And it always showed him the way.

So, on this night, as he walked aimlessly, attempting to soothe his aching heart, he realized that he had ventured deep into the swells of the desert. And he was lost, but he was not worried. He could navigate back to the oasis using the sky just as he always had done before. So, he raised his head and scanned the creamy night sky and turned to where he knew he could find the star. The star that his father had proclaimed to be his so many years ago. There it was. It was always there. The one thing in his life that he could always rely on. His star.

But tonight something was different. Tonight his star was not shining upon him like it had since he was a child. The entire sky was different because of this one star. His star. The star that he knew to be one of the brightest lights in the night sky was not dancing its usual dance of wonder. It was dimming. It was dying right before his eyes. Never before had the man seen a star dim. He spent countless hours, so many nights of his life, learning the stars in the sky, and this was the first time he had ever seen one as it was losing its light.

"How could this be?" the man whispered to himself in wonder. He couldn't look away as he watched his star lose its light, just like a candle fighting to stay lit at the end of its wick. Confusion filled the man's mind as he wondered if he was dreaming. Surely a star could not act in such a way. As his wonder began to cause the breath in his chest to pant, he noticed something peculiar. The star began to mimic his breathing. The light seemed to brighten as he inhaled deeply, and the light would dim as he exhaled. The man was mesmerized and could not break his stare until the howl of the wind grew intense as it rushed past his face. The desert was so calm just moments before. Not a single breeze was in the air. But now the wind screamed an intense scream, blowing the man's garments in every direction. He took his gaze from the night sky and squinted to look away into the distance. The desert had produced a wall that stretched from mountain to mountain in the far distance. *A wall?* thought the man, growing more confused, *There was no wall there before. How can this be?*

It took only a moment for the man to realize that it was a wall of no sorts. It was a sandstorm. A sandstorm like none he had ever seen, growing grand and mighty, higher and wider, violent and more massive as it appeared in the moonlight of the desert. There was no mistaking that this goliath storm was rushing toward him. He turned and looked around himself in hopes of finding shelter, but he knew that he was surrounded by empty desert. He faced the oncoming storm and did all that he could to protect himself from the assault that was going to rain upon him. He pulled his scarf back from the winds and wrapped it around his face as he closed his pale-colored eyes to protect himself, as he had only moments until the sand would brutally make its way to his skin. He stood there in fear as the wind alerted him that the storm was now upon him. Clenching his body to anticipate the pain, he waited for the assault . . . but nothing came. He felt nothing. He could hear the screaming wind all around him, and he knew the storm was upon him, but not a single grain of sand would fall upon his skin. He opened his eyes to make sense of the confusion, and he was bewildered as to what he saw.

The sandstorm was all around him. It danced like a tornado that left a void around him like a halo. He turned around and around to see that he was surrounded in a cyclone of sand as high as he could see, but it was keeping its distance from the wandering man. It wasn't a dream. It all felt too real to be a dream. That he was sure of. But how could this be? What was happening to him on this bewilderingly mystic night in the desert?

Afraid and confused, the man slowly reached his arm out toward the wall of sand that was dancing just a few steps away. Afraid to touch it, he lifted his hand slowly with his fingers extended. The sand gently grazed his fingers as it began to move toward him and dance circles around his arm. The touch was so soothing and calming, unlike any encounter he had ever had with the all-too-familiar desert sand.

The howling wind began to silence as the atmosphere all around him was beginning to calm. The dancing sand that was floating in the air began raining from the sky and spreading around the desert, pushing itself away from the man. Then suddenly a magnificent feeling rushed into the man's chest and straight into his soul. It jolted him upright, and the man began to form a gentle smile. Tears began to form in his eyes as his fear began to subside and was replaced with a sensation of joy. There was no mistaking the wonder that was now upon the man. He knew that he was in the presence of greatness. The light of the world had come to be with this man, and he knew for certain that he was standing in the presence of God.

The man fell to his knees and began to cry. He could do nothing else but weep in the joy of overwhelming emotion and the feeling of elation that filled the air all around him. With his hands held over his face, he felt his heart pounding in his chest as he kept his head bowed low toward the ground.

"My son," a voice called out to him with the most majestic sound that the man had ever heard. It was the voice of God; the voice of God could not be described with words known to any man. "Stand, my son. I have come to be with you."

The man attempted to clear the lump in his throat as he struggled to begin to speak. "My God," said the man, "I am not worthy to be in your presence. Why have you come to be with me? What is it that I can offer to you, my God?" The words were heavy as they left the man's lips, for God could sense the man's sorrow. God knew the sadness that had been growing in the man's heart.

"My child," God spoke in a soft voice, "I have come to be with you because I need you. I know that you are suffering. I know of the sadness that is growing in your heart. I know that you are yearning for something that is being kept away from you. And because of this, that light that shines within you is growing darker. The light that you shine my heavens with has been fading."

Taking a moment to reflect, the man answered to God in a slow and humble voice, "Yes, my God, sorrow has consumed my mind. My heart's desire is far in the distance, and all of my prayers have done nothing to bring it closer." The man bowed his head as he continued to speak, "I am sorry, my God, for it seems that I am doubting my faith. I assure you that I am not. My faith has carried me this far, but I cannot fight the sadness that is shadowing my light. Each day is a battle. Each day is a struggle. And I am growing too weak to fight. I find myself struggling with demons that grow stronger each day. I am sorry, my God, for I am letting you down. But the pain is so great, and I have fallen so weak."

God felt the man's sincerity as the man kept his head bowed and began to speak again, "My son, I am here to remind you that this suffering is what you chose. You asked to endure this. Before this life, when we were together, in my place, you asked to endure for the sake of your growth."

"I asked for this?" the man questioned God.

"Yes, my child. You asked for this. You cannot remember now while you are here in this life, but when we were together before, you asked for all of this. You asked to be a warrior. One that would help save my world. And I told you that it involves suffering. Much that may never be understood. But that through suffering, you will grow to be who I need you to be. You will endure for the sake of your purpose. The pain will make you the one whom you are destined to be.

You rose and asked to be challenged. The warrior in battle who would save my world."

The man fell silent as he would never dare question the great God. However, he felt it to be true. He had asked for all of this.

"There is something I must show you," God began once more. "I must help you to remember. I must help you to understand. You are too great for the purpose. I cannot allow you to fall from your path. Will you come with me? I will take you on a journey."

Awakened by such a request from the great God, the man rose within himself. "Yes, my God, of course I will go anywhere with you. How could I ever deny my God's request?" Then suddenly a light began to shine from above. A warm light that rose as a golden path into the sky above. A path that led to a star. His star. High in the heavens so far away.

The man began to lose sense of the physical world that he knew. He had no realization of the body that he had occupied just moments before. Just a sense of existence remained. A collection of energy that was perfect and shone like a sphere of light. It was the most beautiful feeling. Almost familiar.

He floated up above the world and rose into the cosmos in the presence of God. All the marvels of the universe rushed by him in a beautiful blur of wonder as they made their way to the dimming star that was drawing the man's attention earlier in the night. It was there, before them, burning with a glorious fury. The most miraculous sight that the man had ever seen. The surface of a star that welcomed him without blinding his sight. The sensation was unlike anything he had ever imagined. Stunning. Marvelous. Spectacular. Gases that had been burning for billions of years and solar flares that played like a magnificent orchestra that never stopped. It was all so familiar.

"My star," the man spoke slowly as he stared in amazement. "This is the star that my father named for me so many years ago. It is the most wonderful sight that I have ever seen. But why, my God? Why have you brought me here? What is it that I am to see?"

"It is not out here, my child," God replied, "It is inside."

"Inside?" The man asked with a shock in his voice. "Inside the star? There is such a place? To enter a burning inferno? I would never have dreamed such a feat! But I will follow my God anywhere. Into the star we will go."

The man began to proceed, guided by God's mighty will. Through the violent flames and immense light, they passed a point that was like entering another realm and into an abyss of shadows and light that was an endless round world that was the inside of the star. A spherical phenomenon. The man floated onward until God brought him to a stop to see something that was inside the star. He looked in amazement at the monstrosity that was before him, that God had brought him to see.

It was a machine. Enormous in size. Mechanical in

design. Sprockets and levers and turbines. Wheels that turned and gears that pushed. It was like nothing he had ever seen before. He could not make sense of any of it, but it all seemed to be working so harmoniously. Whatever the machine's purpose, it seemed to be doing it well.

"What is this?" the man asked God.

"This, my child, is the machine," God began to explain. "Every star in the known universe has one. It is the heart of the star. The machine is what keeps the star burning. The machine is what makes the star shine its light."

"A machine? But how?" the man asked with so much wonder in his voice. "Where did such things come from? How does it work?"

"I know you are full of questions, my child. Put your mind at ease. What I brought you here to see will weigh heavy on your heart." God paused a moment before speaking again to help ease the man's thoughts. "You see, my child, long ago I dreamt of creating a world that was filled with a beautiful light. Of only light. A place where darkness did not exist. But for such a place to be real, something had to exist. Something so great that it could consume all the darkness in the entire universe. And I believed this could be real. All of it. For darkness is only the absence of light.

So I had to create enough light to eliminate the darkness. I began, and I created the heavens and the earth, and I filled them with light, and light consumed the entire universe. The most beautiful light. The great cosmos that you see now when you look up at the night sky were not filled with voids of darkness back then. A brightness filled the cosmos for ages because *I* fueled the fires in the night sky. The stars in the sky all shone so brightly that the cosmos were always flooded with light. The universe was nearly perfect. Harmony was always prevalent. The many things were all one. The machines in the stars always had an abundance of fuel from my heart, so their light filled the voids, and darkness was all but unknown."

The man listened eagerly to God's every word as he felt elation within him as he was learning the origins of the universe from the great God.

And God continued to explain, "Then there came a point, my child. A point that has been discussed by many in the world. The point where the one thing became the many things. The many things were all still a part of the one thing, but could be unique as their own things as well. It was from this point that the world you know was born. The heavens and the earth gave birth to your world, and I filled it with my children. For I loved the world so dearly that I handed over the control of the light to you. I rebuilt the machines. All of them. All of the machines in all of the stars that were once fueled by my heart began to attain their power from you. So many stars in the galaxies, so as the many children of the world."

Again, God paused a long while before speaking again. "And this one, my child, this star, this is your star. This is the star that is fueled by you."

The man looked about him once more in amazement. He could see the star pulsating as the machine seemed to contain bursts of energy in rhythm with his own heartbeat. "But how, my God? How can such a thing be? How can I, who am just a man in your world, how can I power such a star so far away?"

"You know the answer, my son. You have known it all along. A great entanglement exists in the cosmos. It connects you to this machine. There is no delay in time. No space needs to be traversed. An instant quantum entanglement between you and this star. It is an extension of you. And the fuel that the machine needs to burn this great star, the fuel that has been diminishing, is causing this star to lose its bright light. You know what it is. You have flourished it for years. But you have begun to fall from this grace. And that is why I have come to see you. Do you know, my child? Do you know what your great fuel is that powers this machine?"

"Yes, my God," the man began to realize.

"Tell me, my child," God asked of the man.

"Love," the man spoke in a sorrowful voice. "Love is the great fuel that powers the machines."

"Yes, my child. It is love. Love is the answer," God proceeded to explain. "You need not understand how. That is not what matters. All you must know is that love is the ultimate force. Love is at the heart of the galaxies. Before I rebuilt the machines, they were all powered by my own heart. They were powered by my love. When I rebuilt the machines, they were to be fueled by the love that came from you. The love that came from all of my children. Early on, the darkness was rare. Love was in abundance because my children knew how to love, and how to be loved. To have love for everyone and to live guided by their hearts. But over time, my children have begun to lose their way. Distractions have arisen, and my children have begun to yearn for desires not of the heart. And the galaxies have come to know the darkness. Where there was once only light from the endless presence of love, there is now vast darkness reaching across the voids."

"My star," the man began to sorrowfully speak, "it was always among the brightest in the night sky since the day my father pointed at it for me so many years ago. It has always shown me the way. Brighter than most . . . that was because of love? That was because of the love that beat inside my heart?"

"Yes, my child," God answered him in a loving voice. "You have been capable of love among the greatest of my children. I have looked upon you with such joy in my heart for all of the light that you have helped shine through the cosmos. You were so close, my child. I had to come see you. I had to try to guide you back to the right path."

"Close?" asked the man. "Close to what?"

"Transcending," God replied.

"Transcending?" he asked as he held onto God's every

word. "How?"

"When love becomes so great, my child, the fuel in the machines becomes immense. The star grows so bright. It comes to a point of such pure and powerful light that it cannot be contained, and the star erupts into a beautiful explosion that sends its love and light to the farthest reaches of the universe touching everything it encounters. This is the destiny for all of the stars. And you have a wondrous name for such an event."

"A supernovae," the man proclaimed with a rasp in his voice. "When love grows so strong, the star goes supernovae." He paused for a while to reflect once again. "I understand, my God. I understand what love means to the universe."

Tears began to form in his eyes as he was coming to realize all that God came to show him, and then realized something more. "The point, my God. The point in time that you mentioned earlier. The point where the one thing became the many. That was you, wasn't it, my God? When you created the heavens and the earth. It was an explosion. An eruption of love. A big bang."

"Yes, my child," God informed the man, "the big bang was me. The big bang was my love for you. It was when my love for you grew so intense and so beautiful that it caused the cosmos to erupt and begin the universe that you know. My love erupted and spread across the entire universe. Covering all of the galaxies. I loved you before I even knew you, my child. For you are a part of me, and I, a part of you. You are one of the many things that come from the one thing. And I need you to love again so that you may be who you are meant to be. The warrior. The warrior of light that was sent to save my world."

"The light warrior," he whispered to himself, remembering the words of his own father. The man stood with tears running down his face as he struggled to find words. "I understand now, my God. I understand why you came to me to show me this place. I have been losing my way, and my heart has been growing dark. I am sorry, my God, I am sorry for doubting. I am sorry for being weak."

"There is no need to apologize, my child. For it is all necessary. It is all a part of your journey. Remember, this is what you asked for. This is what is meant to be." God paused as it all settled onto the man's heart before God spoke these final words. "I dream of a galaxy once again consumed by light, when all of the world can know love. A time when the light will blind out the darkness. And the many things will become one, once again. You are too important to the light, my child, and I cannot let your heart fall. But the decision to love is yours, and yours alone. I know that you are struggling through much suffering. And your faith is being tested. But please know, my child, that I am always with you. When times are most difficult, I am standing over you, making sure you never fall too far. You are always loved, my child. I must watch you from afar, always observing and caring. Hoping that you always choose love. For the sake of the light of the world, may love never leave your heart . . ."

Then it all began to fade. The star and the machine. The cosmos gently rushed by once more as the man was carried back to his home. He was overwhelmed with emotions as he lifted his head. He could feel the world returning all around him as he opened his eyes and found himself in the great desert where his journey began. The great God had come to see him, to remind him of who he really was. And his star, the one that was fueled by the love in his soul, it was floating far in the sky up above him, growing brighter and brighter with every beat of his heart.

the wooden door

A wooden door on an old wooden ship. Once he walked through it, life would never again be the same. It was just a door, no different than any other. Why would he think anything odd? But it was different. This was the door to the galley. The galley that held the sun that would melt his frozen heart.

His journey had begun long ago. He had crossed many seas and traveled across much land, and finally the universe had led him to this door. He paid the universe no mind when he opened the door and ducked his head as he entered the galley. Just another step on another ordinary day. But it wasn't.

The galley was quiet, and empty, apart from one lone passenger standing there looking back at him. The sun that would melt his frozen heart. He stared, without taking a single breath. Then she spoke to him. "Hello," she said with a gentle smile upon her face. And with that, his universe would never be the same again.

They laughed and they danced. They sang and they

sailed. And the ocean roared and the moonlight shone. It was the most beautiful chaos as the world stopped spinning for a single moment to admire the spectacle that was the discovery of love. This was his destiny. He had never been so sure of anything. As the time passed, his heart grew. It had been frozen in ice for so long. He had nearly forgotten the beat of it. The beat that called out to remind him, screaming, "I'm still alive!"

He lived to make her smile. He dreamt to be her everything. Everything made sense. The universe had put the stars in a special alignment, and they pointed directly at her. Until the day came when his heart was ready to present. The day when he would take his own heart and give it to her. It was so full of light. Floating effortlessly out of him. So he took one last breath with it. The breath that he thought would be the last he would ever take without ever sharing it with her. And he took it from his chest, with both hands, and presented it to her. A gentle smile upon his face. But it faded slowly as she did not smile back.

She extended her hands as she lowered her face, and she pushed his heart back to him. "I am sorry," she sobbed, "but I cannot take this." The words pained her to speak.

Bewildered and confused, the man did not understand. He was certain that she loved him. And she most certainly did as she had told him many times. How can this be? Why? But she said nothing as she turned and walked away.

The man looked down at the heart that was beating

in his cold hands, and he watched as the light began to fade. A darkness grew over it as deep scars began to appear. He gave it one last sad look as he returned it into his own chest. How would he continue? How could he have been so wrong?

As the nights grew longer and the time passed on, he fell back into the darkness. Into the place that once again froze his heart. Only one thing remained on his mind. The pain became immense, and the heartache became unbearable. The ice had reclaimed his heart once again. Colder than ever before.

And then on a dark and treacherous stormy night, when he thought he could bear it no more, the sky opened up before the man, and the great God appeared. The man was in disbelief as he stood frozen in place. Everything else in his world fell into the background as he heard the first words.

"My son, if you truly love her, then you will always truly love her. And that love is what saved her. I am sorry that you are suffering."

The man remained quiet, not knowing how to react. He felt the words that God had spoken to him, but he did not truly understand.

And the skies commenced to scream as a storm began to rain over him. Then the next visitor began to appear. A man with a dark shadow for a face. He was ghostly, just as a silhouette, and his appearance was that of the night sky. He walked in the rain, coming closer toward the man. The man stood in place, drenched in water as the thunder roared and the lightning forked in the sky. The shadow-faced man stood before him and asked but one question. "What does your heart say now, child?"

The man paused a moment, not really having to think. And then he replied, sorrowfully, stating what he had been holding on to for so long. "I wish I had never met her." This was his reply. This is what he shouted the second time, repeating with his head raised toward the angry sky. The man returned his gaze to what was before him, and he kindly asked, "Who are you?"

"Child," replied the man with the shadow for a face, "you know me. You know me well. I am many things. I am an angel. I am a demon. I am the world. And I am the void. But today, child, I am the reaper. And I have come to answer your calling."

"My calling?" asked the man. "You mean you can make it true? You can make it so that I never met her?"

"Yes," replied the reaper in a deep and heavy voice.

Hesitating for only a moment, the man called out, "Go on then and do it. Spare me from this misery!"

"I will do as you ask, dear friend. I will set back the sands of time. But first I must give you a gift. A vision of the worlds of choice." The reaper reached out with a bony hand and touched the man on his shoulder.

There was a roar of thunder and a flash of lightning, and the man found himself standing before the ship's wooden door. In the flash of a moment, he saw himself passing through an entire lifetime. Everything that had happened. The love that had blossomed. All the time that he had spent with her. Loving and hopeful. The joy that she brought to him. It felt like a lifetime ago. He also saw the moment he had met the reaper, his heart still broken and mind full of sorrow. Then the vision was of her and the life she would live. She grew happy and loved in the arms of another man. A beautiful family. A home filled with love. She accomplished great things. She made the world a better place. She lived a rich life filled with happiness and surrounded with joy. Then the vision was of himself. Growing old and alone. His heart never healed. He was never able to let go.

When the visions had ended, he stood angry and faced the reaper. "I saw what you wanted me to see. She is happy, and I am not. Now get on with your doing. Make it as you said you would. Spare me this future."

"One more time, child. One more vision. Then I will do as you please."

Once again, the reaper reached out and touched the man on his shoulder. And once again, lightning struck and thunder roared, just as before. And again, the wooden door. But this time he turned. He would not enter. The galley would forever be an unknown mystery. The ignorance would spare him of his misery. The vision was of him and the life that he would have had. A beautiful, loving companion stood by his side. And his heart was filled with light. His days passed with joy, and his life was that of a floating dream. Then the vision changed again. It was her. The woman that he had never met. She was with a man who was not good to her. A manipulator and a cheat. She lived her life feeling empty, unaccomplished, and searching for truth. Happiness had never found its way to her heart.

Then the vision ended, and again he was standing in the rain with the reaper. "Why is she not happy?" he demanded of the reaper. "Why is she living this way?" The man was torn to see the woman he loved living life that way.

"Because, child," stated the reaper, "she never met you. You opened her heart, too. You gave her courage. You made her realize her worth. She would never settle after learning love from you. Just as your universe was never the same after you met her, neither was hers."

The man felt pain, even worse than before.

And the reaper spoke again, "You taught her the greatest thing that anyone could teach. You taught her love."

"Then why?" asked the man with a soft tone in his voice. "Why?" That was the same question that had haunted him since the day she pushed his heart back into his chest.

"I am sorry," said the reaper, "that you may never know. Not all may be answered. But, alas, your own happiness. Look, it was there. Waiting for you. A choice to be made."

"But what about her?" cried the man, "how can her life unfold?"

"That is up to you, child," said the reaper. "But do not fail to recognize the gift."

"The gift?" asked the man.

"Yes, child. The gift. Ignorance," replied the reaper. "A moment after you make your decision, I will take this from your memory. You will start new again from the moment I leave you. You will not be sad for her, for you will have never met her. You will have never known her. You will have never heard her voice. You will have never seen her face."

The reaper paused a moment to observe the stress in the man's face. "You can never be sad for that which you have never known. Ignorance, child, is my gift to you."

A choice stood before the man. He took only a moment as he let out a breath. The man stood in the rain as the reaper summoned the sky. He nodded his head as the lightning flashed and the thunder roared one last time. The reaper faded into the ether, and the man felt ice around his heart.

A wooden door on an old wooden ship stood before him as the reaper had set back the sands. He had made his decision. Another long breath and the man reached a hand forward and opened the door.

The galley was quiet and empty, apart from one lone passenger standing there, looking back at him. "Hello," she said with a gentle smile upon her face.

the alpha tears

"Welcome back," a voice called out. A heartwarming and peaceful voice, although at first its origins seemed strange and distant to the man. He turned and attempted to look about him, but could make out nothing in the darkness he found himself in. *A unique type of darkness,* he thought. These words were the first words he heard. Not the first words he had ever heard, but the first words he heard now. But what was now? He felt as if he had just awoken from a dream, alone in his bed in the dark. He thought to himself, *Is someone there?* Did someone just awaken me from a dream?

Confusion set in further as he could not seem to shake a strange sensation. Not a sensation he was experiencing, but rather a sensation he was lacking. As he tried to gather his thoughts, he realized that he had no awareness of any physical sense. As his mind tried to interpret and search for the feelings that he was so used to, it was failing to relay the sensations of touch and feel. As fear began to set in, he attempted to take a deep breath to calm himself; but again, there was nothing to feel. No breath of air to rush into his lungs. No lungs to fill with air.

So, he called out to the abyss, "Hello?" He knew he was speaking, but the feeling was new. The vibration of his vocal cords was not there. The echo in his ears was not present. All of this was new to him. Different. All of this was different.

"Welcome back? Back to where? Where am I? What happened? Who is out there?"

And again, the voice called out to him, "Our place, my child. Welcome back to our place. Everything will be okay; do not be alarmed. You just arrived, and it is taking a moment to come to you. You finished your time there, and now you are back."

The voice that seemed so strange at first now came with an inviting and welcoming quality. It was no longer the voice of a stranger. It was the voice that the man had heard more than any other. The voice that had answered the man since his beginning. Since all the beginnings. All fear and distress left the man like it was taken away by a gust of wind. And a powerful and stunning feeling replaced that fear like a breeze that flowed through the man that carried his soul into the beautiful sky.

"I do not understand," the man called out, "where am I? Who are you?"

"You know, my child."

"God," cried the man. "My God, I am back with

you. How I have missed you!" Tears filled his eyes and emotions overcame the man as he realized that he was in the presence of God. The emotions were so powerful. So overbearing. A moment that he knew was coming throughout his entire life was finally here.

"I died," proclaimed the man, "just as you told me I would, and I have returned to you. Here, in our place. The place where we last spoke. The place where I left you," He continued with a slow sadness in his voice, "The place where I asked something of you. We are here, again, in our place."

"Yes, my son. I have missed you, too. I have awaited this moment since I sent you to that other place. And now I am filled with joy because you have returned to me." God spoke to the man in a slow and loving manner, for he knew that the man was overcome with emotion and needed to be gently eased back into the heavens where he came from.

So many thoughts came rushing into the man, with too many to make sense of all at once. "I am sorry, my God, everything is still confusing. So much is rushing at me. I do not know where to begin." So many thoughts and so many memories were returning to the man. All overwhelming his thoughts. Here he was, in the presence of the God who gave him life. *What do I say?* thought the man. *Where do I go? What do I do?*

"My son, I know you are full of questions. I have come to meet you here to welcome you back to our place. Do not worry, we have time for everything. Time is everything we have now. You can exist without fear of that anymore."

The man began to calm at the sound of God's words as he was embraced by the most powerful warmth.

"There is something peculiar about you, my son, that I did not see in many of my other children. Something that fascinated me about you. A thought that you carried in your mind throughout your life. A question that you once sought an answer to. Very few of my children fill their minds with such thoughts, my son, and so I have looked forward to meeting with you again for a long time to have this discussion. Do you know the thought, buried there in your mind, that I am referring to?"

"I had so many thoughts, my God," the man replied. "Throughout my life, I questioned so much. Which great thought did I have that has intrigued my God so much?"

"It will come to you, my son," God began. "Allow your mind to recall your life. Allow your memories to cascade over your being here now."

The man began to summon the memories of his life to the new place he found himself in. Memories of being happy and of being sad. Memories of being excited and fearful. So many memories. So many thoughts. *What a life it was,* he thought to himself. He searched for a thought that may protrude unique so that he may engage God in the conversation he seemed eager to have. But with so many thoughts, he could not capture a single one. "I am sorry," he said, "but such a life you allowed me, so many thoughts to go through."

"Your life," said God, "reflect and remember. The thought will come back to you." God paused for a moment, and the man readied himself to engage. "I gave life to you and to so many. Ask yourself now, my son, why I chose to do this. Was it my will? Did I decide to take your soul and send it there, to that place, to have life? Consider that question and you will begin to remember."

The man began to recall a time. A time before the life that God had granted him had begun.

Then God continued to speak, "I gave life to so many, and so many lived in fear. A great question was constantly asked by so many that I gave life to. A question that was always accompanied with fear. But you, my son, you never cared much for this question. You accepted and surrendered to your experience. You looked in the other direction. You lived without this fear, and for that reason I admired your soul so very much. Do you know, now, the question I am referring to? The question asked by the many?"

"Where am I going?" replied the man. "That is the question that my brothers and sisters always asked in fear."

"Yes," replied God. "That is the question that plagues my children for entire lifetimes. I gave them life, and they spend a great amount of time asking themselves, asking of me, where am I going after this life is complete? What is next? What will become of me?"

God continued to explain to the man the thoughts of the people of the world. "It is a just question, my son, and so many ask. But it saddens me that the question is accompanied with fear. Can you tell me why my children are so afraid of the answer?"

"The unknown, God," replied the man. "The unknown of what happens to us after we die. The unknown of truth. It makes us all afraid. I, too, was afraid of the answer to this question.

"The unknown," spoke God. "The unknown brings with it a fear that the answer is not what my children want to hear. Consider this, my son. The kingdom of Heaven comes with it a joy so marvelous that it is unlike any experience imaginable by man. Far greater than anything you could ever imagine. And this kingdom, it is available to all. There will be an end to all suffering in Heaven. Only joy and bliss can exist in this place. Yet my children fear and deflect any discussion of dying throughout their entire lives. This always brought a sadness to me. The road to enlightenment is available to all, and yet the thought of this place causes distress and panic in the hearts of ones to whom I gave life. The idea of death is not easy to cope with for most. It is a tragedy, for life is but a dream for the dead." God paused once again before continuing to speak. "But you, my son, you were not the same. You did not ask me this question. You did not care much for such things as the afterlife. What was it that plagued your mind, my son?"

The man felt as if he let out a smile because he knew

now what God was asking of him. A happiness set in him as he realized the great question was perhaps going to be answered for him. He knew the thought that God was trying to dig out of his mind. "I cared very little for what was to happen after my life. You are right. I always trusted my God. As most around me constantly asked, 'Where am I going,' I refrained from those thoughts. Instead, I thought the true great question is this: 'Where did I come from and where have I been?'"

Joy filled both the man and God as they synced their thoughts together. "Where did you come from?" God proposed to the man. "Very few of my children think this way. Very few look to the past. Most think of it to be irrelevant for it cannot be changed. It cannot be relived. It cannot be manipulated, reversed, nor influenced. And they are right. All of those concerns are true. The past cannot be undone. But you, my son, you spent a lifetime dwelling on this idea. And for that reason, I have come to answer another one of your questions with the great story of your past."

The man felt eager to hear every word God spoke. He awakened his awareness more and more as the creator continued. "There was a time in your life when you debated this question. You tried to formulate an answer using logic and the knowledge that you attained throughout your studies and your experiences. Your thoughts took you to a distinct moment. The moment that you believed was the moment in your life where your question began. Do you know the moment I am asking you to recall?"

"My birth," replied the man, speaking slowly to God, "I contemplated the moment I was born."

"And why did you contemplate this moment?"

"I believed it was the first moment of my existence. If I was to determine where I truly came from, then I thought I must determine what exactly I am looking for. If there is a defining moment that begins my existence, then the answer I am seeking lies before that moment."

The man explained his logic to God and recalled the great many times throughout his life where he struggled with these thoughts. Ideas would come to him. Sometimes a grand thought would develop in his mind, perhaps an answer; but in a moment, it would slip away like the wind, unable to grasp onto, and unable to truly answer his thoughts.

"My birth marked the first moment of my life's existence, and so it was the beginning of my search."

"Your alpha," proclaimed God. "You are speaking of your alpha. Your beginning of life. Yes, my son, that was the beginning of your life, but it was not the beginning of you." God spoke softly once more as the man was led in thought. "When you thought of your birth, your alpha, what did you think of? During your life, when you would call out to me asking your great question, your thoughts focused on an action of your birth. You asked me once about this action. You sought to understand it and refused to believe the answer that science and logic had given to you."

"My tears," said the man, "my tears are what I always thought of. I cried the moment that I was born. Nearly all of us do. It is the first thing we do when we come into the world. I have pondered this action many times. I have dwelled on it as a piece of the puzzle to the great question that I sought to answer my entire life. When I spoke of this to others, I was made to be foolish for asking such an answerable question. I was always told the ways of science have answered this question. They would say that the reason we cry when we are born is because of the stimulation to our newly-developed senses. The cold, the lights, the sounds, the touch. The fluid in our lungs needs to be cleared. The absence of the womb. All of these, I was always told, are the reasons we cry.

"But this was never enough for me. I refused to believe that there was nothing more behind it. The greatest moment that existed at that point in my life had just occurred. My birth. The only moment in my life at that time. I came into the world accompanied by tears. There must be another answer. An answer with the magnitude of the universe. I would not allow science to take that away from me. But sadly, my God, I never concluded another answer. Will you tell me, now, here in our place? Will you tell me why we cry when we are born?"

"My son. My creation. My life. That is why I have looked forward to your return for so long."

God's answer embraced the man. A new sensation overpowered him as he knew he was about to receive a fulfillment of enlightenment that he had sought throughout his entire life.

"You are ready to hear the great answer to your question. The great story that I have waited so long to tell you . . . Your life, my son, was not given to you at my will. It was asked for by you. All lives are. You must understand that your existence did not begin during your alpha birth moment. Instead, you have always existed. Just as I have no beginning, nor do you. You have always been here, not just with me, but a part of me. You are my child; but you, too, are a part of your God. You are a part of this universe. This great experience. You are a part of it, and you are every part of it. All of my children are within me, as I am within them. All connected. Forever. One never-ending mass of energy. Distinguishable by different souls, all a part of the one great soul. Do you understand, my son?"

The man considered God's words, and he answered with a question, "Like a drop of water to the ocean?"

"No, my son, like the entire ocean, in a single drop. I wish more than anything that my children in the world would understand this. But it is difficult to obtain this thought when the way of life I intended has turned so far gone. My son, you are everything. And as I said, you have always existed. We have always been together. I created you in my image. Perfect. All of the souls in all of existence were created perfect. And we all existed as one harmonious being. In glory. And there came a time, my son, when I created the heavens and the earth. I created a special place. The world you just came from? Well, I created this place with perfection in the beginning as well. But perfection escaped from that place." God paused for a moment, as if pondering a sad thought. "And there came a time when you came and you asked something of me. Do you remember that time, my son? Do you remember what it was that you asked of me?"

"Life, my God," the man recalled. "I asked you for life."

"Yes, you asked me for life. You came to me, the perfect soul that I created. The perfect soul that had existed with me forever, and you asked me for life. You asked to be born. You told me that you wanted to go there, to that world. To be born. You wanted to experience life. To live, for a time, in the world that I created. And what did I say to you, my son?"

"No," the man replied to God. "You denied me, and you said no."

"I told you no, my son. I pleaded with you. I did not want to send you there. And you asked me why I did not want to give you life. Why I wanted to keep you here, with me. And I explained. I told you that there, in that place, you would no longer remain perfect. If I gave you life and sent you to that world, you would change."

God went on, "You have existed, perfectly, forever. All the bliss. All the harmony. All the joy. These were the things that we knew together. But there, in that world, there was something else. There was suffering.

I told you that if I gave you life and allowed you to live in that world, that you would live only as you pleased. Only as you chose. And that it brought me great sadness because in that world you would leave me as a perfect soul, and you would change." Again, a great sadness returned to God's voice. "You would lie, you would cheat, you would steal, and you would hurt. You would commit foul acts that would pain me to see. You would suffer and you would harm. You would pillage the earth I created in beauty, and you would lose your way. And you asked me, my son, why? Why would I do such things? Why would I forsake you in that way? You, my God, my creator. I owe everything to you. Why would I betray you?"

"My God," the man spoke, finding it difficult to form the words, "I remember. I remember this conversation now. I remember coming to you and asking this of you. I remember you pleading with me to stay. I am sorry, my God," he said with humiliation, "I am sorry. I should have listened to you." A sadness came over the man. "Will you finish? Will you tell me the rest? Will you tell me, exactly then, why I cried when I entered the world?"

"My son," God began to speak again, "do not be sorry, for I love you. I love you with unconditional love. I am only telling you this now so that you can understand. Understand, my son, that I will never let you down, and I will never keep from you what it is that you truly desire. And so I left the decision to you. I pleaded with you to stay with me, but your desire to experience life was so great. I told you I would grant your request, but that I would ask something of you. I informed you that I would accompany, with your gift of life, another gift. The gift of free will. Upon taking your first breath in your new life, I would grant you the free will that I grant to all of my children. You would be free to live the life I gave you as you please. Your decisions will be yours to make.

"But for free will to be truly free, I must take something from you as well. I must take away all knowledge and memories of your entire existence before the time of your birth. Before the moment that I give you life, you will remember nothing. You will know nothing of this place and your time here with me. I will take that away from you, and I will hold it. I will guard it here, with me, until you return to this place, and then I will give it back to you. And we can continue to exist together once again, only from then on, you will add to that which I took away from you—the experiences and memories that you acquired during your life. The good and the bad. Every part of your life will then be a part of your existence.

"And I will ask something of you. Only one thing. If you insist on leaving this place and going to that world, and I have told you why I do not want you to go, then do one thing for me. One and only one thing. One thing that will root itself in every part of everything else you will ever do. And it is something so simple. This action that I ask of you is Love. Live for love, my son. Love is the reason for all of existence. We have existed here perfectly because of love. It is for love that I created your soul, and if you go there to that world, continue to live only for love. Do not lose sight of that. Do not go to that place and break my heart, my son."

The man's sadness suddenly grew as he remembered his response to God's request, "I promised, my God. I promised you that I would live only for love."

"You promised, my son. You promised me that you would never break my heart and that you would only live for love. And in that alpha moment, my son, that moment when you entered the world, there was an overlap. A fraction of a moment in time just before I took away from you what I told you I must take away, where you were given a glimpse of your life to come in the new world you asked to be sent to. A fraction of a moment where you held with you all the knowledge of your prior eternal existence, and you thought of the last thing you said to me. And you caught that brief glimpse of the world to come, and you saw ahead of you the life you were about to live. And you cried, my son. You cried because you realized in that alpha moment that you made a promise to God that you could never keep."

"I left you," the man wept as he spoke. "I left you, and I broke my promise." Too ashamed to continue, the man stood humbled, not knowing how to go on thinking of how much he must have been a disappointment to God. "I lost my connection to love."

"Yes, you broke your promise, my child; but it was I who never stopped loving you," God spoke with comfort. "You were always loved, my child. And I know that you always loved me, too. And that love has brought you back to this place. It was your destiny to live that life, and your broken promise still led you back to me. Yes, you left this place, but you have never left me. And together, we will always know love."

the summit

The moonlight shadows from the swaying treetops seemed to be following him. The man walked without purpose through the night forest. He was deep in thought as he looked up at the star-filled sky. *Why is it so hard?* he thought to himself. "This life, this time here," he spoke aloud to himself as no one else was there to hear, "I miss happiness," he whispered under his breath as he slowly bowed his head.

He continued on his way through the dimly-lit path in the forest as he felt sorrow in his heart. The man had been through many hard times, and lately they seemed to be getting more and more difficult to survive. So much was going wrong. He began to question everything. He questioned why he tried so hard. He questioned why he should even continue. His heart would weigh heavy at the mere thought of the questions that wandered into his mind.

The sounds of the night came and distracted him for moments at a time, but they were only moments, and the sorrow would quickly return and take its place in his mind again and again. The shimmer of the stars captured the gaze of his heavy eyes as his head leaned back, and he asked of the night sky, "Is all of this suffering for a purpose? Is there something out there for a greater good?"

As he stood there embracing the breeze of the night air, the moon casting shadows upon his face, the sound of the trees drew his attention. The earth all around him began to awake. The enchanting nature scene around him was taking on a life of its own. The trees seemed to have breath as they pulsated in the wind. The faint streaks of white in the distant night sky seemed to become milkier. The breeze that was earlier only flowing through his long hair now seemed to be dancing about him, making him feel light on his feet. Concern for what could happen next began to make the man anxious. A fear was making its way into his mind as his heart began to race. Confused and worried, the man closed his eyes and drew a deep breath. Then somehow, in an instant, all he felt was calm. In fact, the man had never felt more at peace before in his entire life. A smile broke out on the man's face as he slowly realized what had just happened. Something marvelous. A great presence became known to the man. His smile began to widen.

"God?" the man asked with many tones in his voice. He laughed at himself as he realized that he posed a question of doubt and soon spoke again to make the statement more clear. "God." The feeling was so powerful that there was no reason to doubt.

"My child," God spoke to the man, all alone in this majestic place, "I have come to call upon you."

God's presence brought great confusion to the man as he did not know how to react. Many thoughts raced through his mind as he struggled to find the right words. Which thought to articulate first? In which manner to do so? And then he began, "You are here to call upon me?" asked the man. His bewilderment arose high as he questioned himself. "My God, but it is I who often calls upon you. My creator. My light. I am humbled by your presence, but surely you have come to the wrong man for whatever it is that you seek. Surely the one whom God calls upon must be one of great might and strength, of tremendous honor and courage. And I," he paused, "I am just a man . . ." He finished his words with sadness in his voice, as if he felt that he was a disappointment to God. Assuring himself, he thought that surely he could not be the one who God must be seeking.

"No, my child. It is you. You are the one who I have come to see. You are the one I need." God gently embraced the man to comfort him in his thoughts. "I am in great need, my son, and you must help me right what has gone wrong."

God's words were the most genuine the man had ever heard. Although still lowly with doubt, he would not dare to question God again. If he was to be called upon, then he must rise to God's side and he must aid God's needs.

The man stood tall as he prepared to answer God. He

took a long breath with his eyes closed as he felt a new self-worth that he had never felt before.

"What is it, my God, that you need from me now? What can I do to serve you? I, who am inadequate and meager. I, who has pledged my soul to my God, what is it that I am called to do?"

God was slow with a reply as there was self-doubt in the man's eyes. A long moment went by before God once again spoke with a gentle tone, "What I ask of you will not be easy, my child. But it is more imperative than all else in this world. More crucial than anything else in this life. It will determine the survival of the world that I have created. The world that I love."

The intensity of God's words felt heavy on the man's ears. God could see once again that the man doubted in his own abilities to carry on the task that was to be asked of him. Surely, it would be of great magnitude. Then God continued, "This task I will tell you of, but not here. Not in this place. You must travel to the summit of a mountain, my child, where I have chosen to bestow upon you the greatest of tasks in all of the land."

"A summit?" the man asked of God. "Where is this summit? And how am I to get there? My possessions are meager and my resources are few."

God was silent for a moment before speaking once more, "The summit is far and the journey will be strenuous. It lies in the place where the earth kisses the sky. Where the clouds are below you and the cool air is thin.

You know of this place; you have heard stories of it before. You have everything you need, and I have no doubt that you will arrive. I will be there waiting for you at this place. And there I will tell you the great task that I must ask of you." The words faded into the wind as the man's attention returned to the forest as he looked all about him. God was gone.

The man looked all around to find himself alone once again. The sounds of the night returned in every direction. The moonlight cast the way through the trees as he stood there in awe of what had just happened. Once again, he looked toward the sky, and he clenched his hands in anticipation of the journey. He knew of the summit where God had instructed him to go, and he let out an overwhelming sigh as he knew this place to be far and a journey of great difficulty. But he felt the great importance of what he must do. After all, how often is one told that he is needed at God's side?

And so, he took his first step forward, moving toward the edge of the forest and reuniting with God on the summit that peaked on the other side of the world. He walked through the night as dawn appeared in the distance, stopping to rest for the first time. His spirits were still high as he continued to feel the importance of being called upon by the great God. He had rested enough and stood to continue, but trouble appeared before him. A group of stout thieves appeared on horseback to cut off his path.

They stood tall above him, swords ready in their hands as they shouted with rage, "Your possessions or your life, young traveler, the choice is yours!" They all drew their blades from their sides as they laughed at his misfortune. There was no compassion from the men as they watched the man shiver with distress.

A great fear consumed the man's heart as he began to plea, "Please, spare me. I have nothing to offer; I am on a journey to meet—" But he was cut off by one of the men as the thief jumped off his horse and struck the man with a blow.

The bandit circled him as he sensed his fear. He knew the poor traveler had nothing of value, but showed no mercy as he demanded, "Give me your boots!" as he placed his sword on the man's neck.

"They are yours," surrendered the man, "please spare me my life."

As the man stood there painfully barefoot, he could see the thieves were deciding if they would take his life as well. They appeared before him as a band of evil self-appointed judges and executioners. His head bowed low as he anticipated the worst. Afraid to look too long at his capturers, he noticed their gaze fade beyond him, over his shoulders, in the distance as they turned to face away. Their jovial arrogance quickly subsided as they seemed to be struck with fear. He turned to see what was there as they made a quick sound and galloped away. He saw nothing behind him and let out a sigh of relief as he gathered himself from the ordeal.

Alone he stood there. "I must continue," said the man. Discouraged and barefoot, he walked on. The rough earth was covered with stones of jagged edges as he endured pain under his feet. But he still walked on, for he knew he had an appointment too important to miss. Blood dripped from his feet as they had no protection on his long and strenuous journey. Then, finally, he exited the forest to find himself at the edge of an ocean. His destination lay far across the treacherous, salty sea. Wild beasts and predators swam freely before him, causing him greater fear. His body was already aching and defeated from the long journey out of the forest. He took a step forward to test the water with his bloody feet. It was icy and unwelcoming, just as it looked. He stopped to look up at the sky as if to expect help to appear for the great challenge before him. But none came. Nothing changed. No great chariot appeared in the sky to carry him along. No voice called with an answer. Not even a ray of sunlight to help warm his cold body.

"I must go on," was all he could say as he shook his head.

One step forward, and he was ankle deep in the water. Another step and the water was above his knees. One final step and the man found himself exerting his energy to stay afloat as he swam forward through the unfamiliar sea. One stroke at a time. Breath after breath. He kicked and reached and swam until the land behind him was gone. He could not turn back even if he wanted to, for he would not remember where to go. Exhaustion was setting in as he struggled to stay afloat. There in the distance a mighty ship appeared.

Too weak to shout for aid, he waved his arms in the air. The mighty ship cut through the water with great sails made of silk. The wooden hull was bold and rich, and the man could see people joyful and laughing as they walked along the deck.

They have it so easy, he thought to himself. *They are crossing this ocean in comfort and leisure, and I am suffering as I struggle to meet a call from the great God. Injustice*, the man felt as he watched the ship sail further and further away toward a marvelous golden sunrise on the horizon. The man kicked at the water to keep from sinking and drowning as anger set into his mind. The ship would offer him no aid.

"Why am I enduring such troubles as the world around me lives in such riches?"

The might of the ocean grew heavier and heavier on the man as he once again found himself defeated and alone. Then the beasts of the ocean appeared for an unfriendly greeting. The giants swam in circles around him, showing their massive teeth to express to him their intentions. Thoughts of surrender entered his mind as he treaded water with fatigue.

"Can I give up?" he asked himself. "Can I stop going on and let the ocean have me?" He felt sad at asking himself this question, but he knew he was only human, and that his energy would surely run out. "No, I must continue. As long as I have a beat of blood still left in me, I must continue." And he reached and kicked. Arm after arm. Leg after leg, doing everything he could to fight off the beasts as their teeth pierced his skin as he screamed with pain.

This is the end, he thought to himself, *this is where I fail.* And then, all of a sudden, a tremble was felt, and a great wave came before the man and lifted him to great heights. He was carried above it as it crashed down on the beasts and chased them away.

"What great luck!" he shouted as he realized he had just escaped death once more.

The man made his way through the ocean until fatigue began to get the best of his aching body. The long journey through the cold water had exhausted him, and he had little in him to go on. As he took another breath, fearing it could be his last, the clouds parted and the sun appeared before him. The light falling upon his face gave him comfort and warmed him as the earth seemed to rest and calm. And then an ocean current seemed to appear at his back to help float him upon the edge of the water. He had become so buoyant floating in the salty sea. So much easier it was to swim through the ocean as the land appeared for the first time before him. It was just the sight he needed to give him hope to continue on his journey.

After a great time had passed, he washed up ashore and crawled on his hands and knees. Finally out of the water, he collapsed on the sandy earth that had been there waiting for him. Spitting up water and gasping for air, he was grateful. He no longer needed to exert his energy to keep from drowning. He laid on his back as his chest pouted, struggling to come to a rest. "God is waiting for me," the man said aloud to himself.

He caught one last breath as he stood and turned to continue on his journey. But another sight of discouragement lay there before him. A daunting vast desert as far as the eye could see now stood in his way. A great plain of nothing but sand and sunlight was between him and the mountain where he was to go to meet with God again.

Discouraged and full of doubt, once again he looked to the sky. "I must go on," he managed to say as he took his first step into the tiresome sand. Still barefoot and battered with wounds all over his body, the man walked step after step toward the summit where he was to meet God. His emotions had changed greatly since the start of his journey. He began with a drive of passion the day they first met. So inspired and motivated to embark on this journey. Perhaps, he admitted to himself, he had expected the road to his destination to be lined with golden streets, and all that he desired would be there in abundance along the way. After all, he was on a mission from God. The least God could do was aid him along the way.

But the opposite had been true. The journey had been far from pleasant. It was full of pain and suffering, and worst of all, it was wretchedly lonesome. All the while, it had been a reminder of his greatest struggle. His struggle with loneliness. But still he continued and moved on through the desert. And dehydration began to set in.

"What I would give for just one drink of water," the man said aloud to himself. His steps seemed heavy, and he stumbled forward instead of marched. There again, in the distance, he spotted a caravan of royals. Covered wagons and camels were all traveling together as the man could see emeralds and rubies shimmering from the wardrobes of those in attendance. Gold carafes filled with water were being passed around in the group to quench the thirst of the royals passing through the desert. The man fell to his knees as he waved his arms in the air and cried out for help. But the royals dismissed his cries and kept to themselves. The elite continued on their parade and they paid him no mind. No aid would come to him. No gold carafes to offer him a drink.

Once again weary and exhausted, the man struggled to find the will to continue. Defeat was no longer a stranger on this journey, but rather a common face. Too weak to walk on, the man fell to his knees and began to crawl to make his way out of the desert. So much time had passed since he had first entered this wasteland. Once again feeling so defeated, the wind at his back seemed to whisper into his ears. It was a comforting feeling. One that he had not felt in a long time. It caused him to raise his chin and look far into the distance to see that the end was in sight. A babbling creek of cool water echoed sounds in the distance.

"Just a little farther," he told himself. Crawling forward on his hands and knees, he went on until finally he collapsed at the side of the creek where the desert had ended. He was so weak that even taking a drink was a great struggle.

The man rolled over onto his back and stared at the

sky. Dark clouds began to move in, and the earth began to roar. Just moments after he began to feel encouraged, a great storm appeared above him and the winds began to scream by his ears. With no shelter visible in any direction, the storm began to batter the man in his place.

The thought of defeat entered the man's mind. *It has become too much,* he thought, *this is my breaking point.* He would no longer go on. Where was the justice? Where was his aid? God came to him and asked him for great service, but now where was God as the man lay there beaten and weak. Defeated and devastated.

Anger set in as he let out a shout, "Damn you!" he lashed out as he pumped his fist in the air. "Damn you for abandoning me when I need you most! When I am on my way to do your bidding! When I, who is meager and weak, need you to carry me, you are not here!" The anger soon turned to sadness as tears began to run down his face. One last time, he said it: "Damn you," but softly this time as the rains began to subside. "I am sorry," he cried, "but I am done. I will go on no farther. Find someone else. Leave me be and say no more." Tears continued to fall across the man's face as thunder forked in the sky. "I told you when you met me that I am not good enough to be the one you need."

As the rains stopped pouring and the lightning moved away in the distance, a woman appeared in the distance. She was walking toward the man as he stood and he blinked to focus his eyes. "Why are you saddened?" she asked calmly as she approached. She was fair-skinned and looked healthy, and her voice was angelic as it sang into the man's ears.

"I have failed God," the man slowly replied with a lowly tone in his voice. "God called upon me to meet him to receive some great task, and I have failed. I have given up on him. I have cursed his name and I have foiled his plans. I do not want to continue. I am not worthy of this life. And if this is the way that life is going to continue, I want nothing to do with it." The man lowered his head in shame as the feeling of failure settled into his heart.

The woman stepped closer and placed a gentle hand on his shoulder. Her presence was restful. He could feel her energy as the only comforting feeling that had been in his life since the day God came to speak to him. Again, she spoke softly, "God came to me once," she said as she broke out a smile. "Long ago, when my life was in shambles. I could hardly care for myself, yet God appeared and asked greatness of me. God sent me off on a journey, and the same has been done to you. It was a time in my life that I needed God the most, yet I was sent off to save the world in some great quest."

Wiping tears from his eyes, the man looked up to marvel at the woman's beauty. She seemed so accepting of the world around her. She seemed to be happy among the world of chaos that lay all around them. She stood tall above him and her hand continued resting on his shoulder as he remained on his knees. With a lump in his throat, he struggled with words, "God called upon you?" he asked. "Did God send you off alone, too, to face near death and battle great challenges?"

She paused for several moments, taking her gaze from his eyes to the land that lay beyond him and peering over his shoulder toward the distance as she gathered her thoughts. Another warm smile appeared on her lips, to almost a grin, and then a gentle laugh. "No," she replied, "God did not send me off alone." Her words seemed to come from a vision, as if she realized that she would have been wrong if he had asked her this same question a long time ago.

The man began to turn to see the vast wasteland that lay behind him as he felt a guilty envy for the woman he just met. He turned from side to side to gesture his solitude before he answered, "You were with company, then, while I am struggling alone?" Once again, the sadness of his situation drew near his heart, and tears began to form in the corners of his eyes. "I have damned and I have cursed. I have given up on my journey. It is too late for me. Thank you for your comfort, but it is too late for me. You can leave me be."

"Very well," said the woman, "but first, will you stand and face me before I go?" the woman asked of the man, thinking it was a kind request. "There is something I must tell you. Something you must hear." She looked into his eyes and assured him of her sincerity. "You are why I am here, and I must give you something before I depart."

Confused and bewildered, the man stood to his feet, face to face with the stranger he had just met. Unsure of how to respond. He just stood and patiently waited as she stared upon him with a loving gaze. He felt that the entire world was staring at him. Emotions ran wild through the man's soul as his tears of sadness quickly turned into tears of passion. The energy that was rushing through his body was outlandish to him. He could not explain such a feeling in words, nor did he attempt to. He just stood and marveled at the woman who was a stranger standing before him.

She opened her arms as he did the same, and the two strangers embraced each other for what seemed to be forever. Together they cried and together they rose. Spirits flew high as their emotions grew wild.

As they stood there in the comfort of each other's arms, she whispered into his ear as she gazed beyond his back, "You are not alone."

Her words felt like assurance as he tightened his grip. He did not know why, but he believed her. Moments went by until he felt a new energy consuming his mind. Onward with his journey he would go, he thought, as the two began to exit their embrace.

"Go on," she said. "God understands your moment of weakness, here, in this place. And if you truly believe that you have derailed God's plan for your life," she said as she took one last look, gently brushing the hair back from the man's face with a gentle laugh, "then rest assured, you beautiful fool, you are not that powerful."

The man stood in place as the woman disappeared in the distance. "I must continue," he said to himself, "I must make it to the summit." With a newfound inspiration, he walked and he walked. Still battered and bloodied, he went on. Much time had passed as he came to the last part of his journey.

"There is the place," he exclaimed as he pointed up into the distance. "There is the place where God is waiting for me." The summit was there, in fact, atop a boundless mountain. A tall mountain with no easy passes for any who would attempt to reach its great peaks. *One last challenge,* he thought to himself. *One last mountain to conquer.* And he moved on, one step at time. Onward and upward, again exhausted and near death, he managed to find energy for every step. Perseverance would get him through it. Fatigue would set in and cause him to collapse, but each time a wind at his back would assist him on this route as he reached for ledges to grasp as he pulled himself up the side of the mountain.

Climbing upward, ascending toward the sky, he was using every last bit of energy that remained. The climb was beating his body and he was aching with pain. Until finally, there it was. The end. The summit that God had asked him to reach. With his last steps he had made it. He stood there, above the entire world, and let his head fall backward as he looked upon the sky. He had some moments alone to bask in his accomplishment. Then once again, just as before, the world around him had come to life, and God's presence was there.

"I am here, God," the man said to his creator. "I have suffered and I have endured. I have been beaten and I have been battered. I have seen misery and I have seen defeat. I have been abandoned and I have been robbed. I have felt empty and I have felt pain. I have been humbled, and I have been humiliated. I have given up, and I have gone. I did it all. Alone. And now I am here, God. I am here."

A mix of emotions of anger and triumph ran wild through the man's blood. Surely, God must understand the feelings radiating from the servant that was called upon.

"Yes. You are here," God replied to the man. "Yes, you suffered all of those things. And yes, you are here. And I know you are full of anger and a feeling of query; why did I let you suffer through all of those times?"

The man stood tall as he piqued his full attention to God. "Yes!" he shouted, "Why?! Why, my God? What did you call me here to do? What do you need from me that is so imperative that it will save your world?! And why must I have suffered so greatly to come to this place to receive this message?!"

"Because," answered the great God, "you are here." And then a silence consumed the air.

Confusion set in as the man began with his reply "I do not understand, God. Yes. I am here. But I do not understand. Will you tell me what it is that you wish of me?"

"Before I tell you my wish, let me first tell you why I asked you to come to this place." God began to explain, "This place is far from where I first came to see you, and many obstacles stood in your way. You had to endure great tragedy and suffering all along the way. Many times, you thought you would not make it, I am sure. I am afraid that all of it was necessary."

"Necessary?" asked the man. "Necessary for what? Why was it necessary to beat me and to break me?"

"For your soul, my child. It was all necessary for your soul. For you to learn and to experience and to mature. To prepare you for your great purpose. I will soon tell you what great feat I am to ask of you, but please understand, my child, that I first had to ready your soul to live out your task. You endured much suffering along this journey, this I know, but none of it was in vain. Nothing is to chance. It was all for a great purpose. And that purpose was for you to experience. You must first understand suffering before you can know joy. Your soul must be tried and tested so that it can successfully carry out my task. For it is no easy task at all . . . When the thieves stole your boots and you begged for assistance, tell me, what lesson would you have learned if you had not felt their pain? When you saw the men on the ship, and you wished to join them across the sea, tell me, what maturity would you have gained if they would have pulled you aboard? When you fought the beasts of the ocean, what strength would you have acquired if you had not defeated them on your own? When you struggled to cross the desert and the royals denied you water, tell me, what lesson did you learn when you made it to the creek? When the mountain stood tall before you, and you wished for an easy pass to the top, tell me, what would you have gained had one been granted to you?"

The man listened and pondered as he remained confused. "I don't understand, God. What do these things have to do with my purpose? And why did I have to suffer so greatly alone?"

"Because, my son, you are here. Just as you exclaimed to me, you are here. You were taken to your breaking point, time and time again. You stared defeat in the face, and when you thought you would fail, and when you thought you would no longer go on, you did. And you are here. You always managed. You always triumphed. No matter how horrendous it became, you always made it. That is your lesson, my child. You are here."

The man began to realize what he was being told. He had always made it. He conquered every obstacle that he had ever faced in his entire life. Standing there with a wild beating heart, proof is this great feat.

"And don't you see, my beautiful child, you were never alone." A motion from behind him caused the man to turn and see a great sight. Countless angels were there in great glory at his back. "I was with you every step of the way. I was always at your back with my army of angels, ensuring that you would never fail. When you feel that you will fall to the bottom, rest assured, my child, I am always there to catch you. I am always there to help you along the way. I will never allow you to endure anything beyond that which I know you will not conquer. Like a warrior in my battle, you will always rise and you will always triumph. In this life, and the next. And when you can walk on no more, I am always there to carry you."

More tears fell from the man's face as he realized this was the truth. God was always there, over his shoulder, standing beyond to protect him. To carry him when he could no longer carry himself. Speaking slowly, he said, "Thank you, my God. Thank you for this life. I am sorry for doubting. I will not doubt again. I am here. I understand my great sufferings, and now I am ready. Tell me, my God, what is it that you must ask of me? What did you bring me to this place to do?"

"The answer you seek, your great purpose, my child, the one that will save my entire universe, is simply this . . . Love." God's words fell softly on the man's ears as he opened his eyes. "Love all, my child. Spread love throughout the entire world. Radiate it to those too weak to love themselves. Those in doubt. Those in hunger. Those in need."

"To love the entire world?" he asked in bewilderment, not knowing how to react. "but I am just—"

God interrupted, "A man, my child. You are just a man that God has created. A man with a heart that is capable of setting my world on fire. My own heart. And you have gone for too long holding back that love, for my world needs you. There are many in this world who need you. They need your love. Go, my child, and break the hearts of stone. Go and make the darkness bright. Be the love that my world needs. For I created this world in my image. An image of love. And the light that I lit so long ago has dulled and begun to fade, and my children have begun to lose their way. You, who is now ready and matured from your great suffering, can save them by loving them. This was my gift to the world. An endless amount of love to all who would accept it. It is all around you in great abundance. Nothing must be sacrificed on the left to attain love on the right. All energy can become love, and the world can be a marvelous place. And now, my child, you know your great purpose. Your eyes have been opened and you have the power to choose. My will is only a request, not a demand. You may go on from this place and live as you please. Always remember, my child, I am always there. Every time you love another, you will see me in their face. You will never be alone. I know you are capable, my child. I know, because you are here."

the rose garden

S he did not cry. Not a single tear. Not even once. She
would travel far every morning to the countryside
to be with her loving mother. Her mother who had
fallen ill. Her mother who was dying. She was sad from
the moment she would wake and all along her journey;
but still, she did not cry.

Every day, the young woman would arrive at her
childhood home. It was not a house. It was a home.
A humble and quaint English red brick home. And
there she would find her mother pruning the leaves on
a rose bush that grew below a window at the front of
the house.

This particular day, she was welcomed by her teary-
eyed mother and the two went inside to rest and
reunite again. The illness was winning the battle and
her mother was continuing to fall. And as the days
passed and the nights grew longer, the mother fell
deeper into herself and could no longer leave her bed.
When the young woman was pruning the rose bushes,
her mother would sleep; the young woman would sit in

a chair at the window before the rose bush and hold her hand. She would look gently upon her mother's resting face. But the young woman could not see the defeated face that was before her. No. Instead, she could see the face of the young mother who raised her. That young mother who was beautiful and filled with life. The young mother who would run her fingers through her hair when she would lay on her lap as a little girl. The young mother who made her daughter the center of the universe. The young mother who was her first love. This was the only face that the young woman could see. And it was beautiful.

As her mother slept, the young woman would sit in silence. Her mind was like a theater of endless memories with the woman who lay beside her. The feeling would push its way up her throat, and she would fight it off. Still, she would not cry. Instead, she would turn away from her mother's resting face and she would stare out the window.

There was the rose bush. The one that her mother had planted many years ago. The one that her mother was so proud of and adored. For years, she could remember her mother caring for that bush. Watering it when the sun would shine. Pruning it when it became too wild. And admiring its beauty when it would flower. Ever since her mother had fallen into her illness, the bush had been neglected. The once adoration-worthy rose bush that flowered bright with radiant color now only yielded a single flower. A single, perfect red rose that protruded high above the thorny branches that extended into the ground below. Although it was alone on the bush, it was magnificent. Every petal so lush and vibrant. Each laying homage to the petal before it as they stood strong and reached for the sunlight in their wondrous circle around the centered pistil. It was truly perfect, if there ever was a perfect rose.

The young woman spent countless days admiring the rose, watching its petals flourish in the sunlight, smelling its fragrance when the window was open. The rose was more than just a flower to her. It stood for something. Something important that she had to hold on to. She was grateful to admire it as there was a warm comfort that would radiate from its beauty.

As she knew it would, her mother's illness grew dire. The sands of time were filling the bottom of the hourglass, and soon her hand would not be there to hold. But still, the woman spent time admiring the rose. The rose that would help hold back her tears. Always sitting at the window at the front of the house beside her mother's bed. Saddened by the thoughts of her mothers' pain, she watched as a single petal fell from the rose. The first petal the flower had ever shed. She watched as it danced through the air, gliding back and forth and spinning around and around as it made its way down to the earth below. She stared at the petal and knew the others would follow, and soon the rose would be no more. Each day her mother fell further and further away as the young woman held her hand; and at the same time, she watched the flower shed more and more of itself.

Then finally, the day came when the young woman held her mother's hand as she took her last breath. She and her mother were caught in a gaze and her mother gave her one last gentle smile. She whispered as she closed her eyes for the very last time, "It's beautiful." And she was gone.

A great sadness fell over the young woman. Her chest grew immensely tight and the lump in her throat felt like a boulder. She knew this time would come, but still nothing could prepare her for such a feeling. Her mother was gone, and still she fought back her tears. She would not cry. She turned away to the window and all that she would see was that rose. Only a single, lonely petal remained. What was once a wondrous red rose full of life and admirable beauty was now only a single petal clinging to a flower on a bare, thorny bush. And then, as she was watching, a gentle breeze came and the last petal blew from the bush and gently fell to the earth below.

The young woman could hold back her emotions no longer, and she began to weep. Her mother's dear friend was there helping to look after the home in her final days. She came to comfort the young woman when she noticed the scattered rose petals that lay on the ground. She saw the tears on her cheeks and the sadness in her heart and the friend knew that rose was much more than just a flower.

The two embraced each other for a long moment until the friend broke the silence, "Come with me, child," she said to the young woman as she took her hand and led her to a door on the other side of the house. "All this time, you have been admiring that beautiful rose. That single rose in the bush at the front of the house. Your mother's rose bush that has been dying. It was such a beautiful rose bush. For years, it brightened all of our lives. It made us smile and it warmed us with its presence. And it was down to its last rose, and now the last petal has fallen and the rose is gone. We wish it would not leave. We wish the rose could flower forever so that we may love it as it brings love to us."

She opened the door and led the young woman to the back of the house where she had not been in many years. And there she revealed something marvelous. On the back side of the house, through that door, there was a sea of rose vines growing down the side of the house, creating the most beautiful rose garden that the woman had ever laid eyes on. It was endless and perfect in every way.

"You see, my child, the rose is not gone. It is never gone. While you wept over each falling petal, the rose was guiding its roots along a journey. Through the earth, along its life. Climbing up the brick walls of the house, inching its way forward, little by little, until it crossed over. Over to the other side of the house. The other side, where the sun is even more beautiful, and the rose could bloom in glory like it was always destined to do."

the gift

Once there was a soul that existed in God's universe. A soul that was filled with love and did everything it could to spread that love around the world. And one day God was admiring this soul and was so moved by the love and passion that this soul emulated that God decided to grant this soul a gift. But what a gift it must be to present to such a worthy soul! God realized that the gift must be one of God's creations and not something that existed in the ordinary world. So God set out to create something. Something marvelous. Something spectacular for the world to adore. God began by going to angels. And from the angels God acquired beauty. The kind of beauty that makes the heart leap. And next God went to the nobles. And from the nobles God was bestowed wisdom. The kind of wisdom that shows us the way. Then God went to the stars. And the stars gave God the light. The light that always overcomes the darkness. Afterward, God went to the earth. And the earth gave God kindness and warmth. The kindness and warmth that is felt from the divine. Then the flowers of the world arose. And they gave God a fragrance. A fragrance that could stop time. Then God went to the heavens. And the heavens gave God honesty and virtue. The kind that would save the world. And finally, God took from within. And God produced love. A love so immense that it could last forever with never an end in sight.

God had acquired a collection. So many things, all in God's hands. All for the creation of the gift. God combined the many things for the soul that God set out to reward. And the result was astounding. The result was you. God created you, as a gift for me.

the weight

She held her hands over her face as the tears ran down her cheeks. "Why?" She would ask herself. "Why do I get hurt so much? Why do I continue to put my heart into this world, only to suffer time after time?"

She lived a life that was righteous and honorable, doing all that she could to be selfless without ever even considering anything else. She did it because it was in her heart to live this way. She did it because it was who she was. Never seeking a reward for her actions. Never expecting acknowledgment from anyone. She was pure and her intentions were good. Yet she carried such heavy burdens throughout her days. So many crosses to carry. And, finally, it became too much. She feared the weight on her shoulders was becoming too great, and perhaps it was time to give up. Perhaps the weight would crush her. And so she began to cry. The thought of giving up was too much for her and she fell to her knees and she wept into her hands.

Desperately, she cried out again and again for answers,

yet none would ever be granted to her.

"Why do I continue to hurt after living this way? Why can't life be fair to me?" Then she asked herself the hardest of questions, "Why do I continue to live?"

The dark thoughts that ran through her mind only made heavier the weight on her shoulders. She cried deeper into the darkness. And the weight began to feel like a mountain pressing her down into the earth, too heavy to carry any further. So she closed her eyes and she accepted the darkness, her hands pressed against her face. She had decided. She was going to give up.

And then it happened. Something odd. Something delightful. The weight was gone. Not just some of it. But all of it. The weight of the entire world that she had been carrying for so long had disappeared. All at once. She felt it all being lifted from her body. From her soul. The feeling was freeing. It was liberating. Such a wonder. It was beautiful.

"But how? Did I die?" She asked herself. "No. Certainly I am still here. I can feel the beat in my heart. I still exist. I am still alive."

But it was all leaving her. The burdens. The weight. It was floating away. As if it were melting off of her and she was beginning to feel weightless. As if she were floating in the darkness.

The darkness. It was still there. Then she realized that her hands were still held over her face. Covering her eyes. So she removed them. And she saw it. The light. The immense light that was all around her. It was marvelous. A bright, warm light that drove out every bit of darkness that surrounded her a moment ago.

"What was happening? Is this real?" Her thoughts were everywhere. At first, she was afraid. The world she had been in moments ago was now gone. And there was no explanation for it. Her heart began to beat faster and harder. What was this new place? This strange new world? She turned about and realized she could not feel her footsteps on the ground below. Only weightless steps. Floating movements. It was so liberating. So euphoric. So much so that her stress began to fade. She began to feel happiness and her heartbeat ran rampant with joy. A feeling that she had not felt in so long. A feeling that she had missed so immensely. A feeling that she had longed for.

Then an unmistakable feeling settled into her soul. It all made sense and she smiled. A smile so intense it hurt her face.

And she called out to nowhere, "Hello, God."

"Hello, my child," God called back.

Of course God was there, coming to see the child who needed him in her life at a time when she was so lost. The world around her was gone, and God had brought her to the place of light. To God's place, where the creatures of the world would come when it was necessary throughout their existence.

"This place," she began softly, "I remember this place. We were here together. Before I came to the world, we were here together in this place. Weren't we?"

"Yes, my child. This is the place where we were together before I gave you this life. This is the place where we always come together. Many times before. And many times to come. This is the world of light."

"The world of light," she replied as she reflected. It was slowly coming back to her. Being in this place with God the last time. It was years ago, and she couldn't quite recall it. "And you have brought me back here again, now. Why, my God? Is my life over? Did you bring me here because I decided to give up?"

And again, she began to weep. "I am sorry, my God. I have let you down, haven't I? I have given up on the life you granted to me. I gave up on your gift. I am so, so sorry. But it was too much. It all became too much. The suffering was so heavy. I could not remember happiness. And I could not go on any further. Will my God forgive me?" The tears continued as the thought of letting her God down began to weigh her down once again.

"Sweet child. Rest your heart," God said to her with comfort. "I have never given up on you. No. Your life is not over. Your life is far from over. I need you to live your life. It's far too great to allow your life to end now. You did not let me down, you beautiful creature. You are living just as we had agreed."

"We had agreed?" she asked, confused. "We agreed to this life? To this suffering? But when? And why? Why so much suffering? Why so much weight?"

"When we were in this place, before, my child, the

last time we were here together. You and I. The real you. The one that rests inside that heart I gave you." God spoke as she tried to remember. "Be calm and stand tall, and I will show you again what it is all for."

The woman rested her heart and grew more attentive as God brought wonder to the world of light. All around her, images began to appear. Floating images everywhere. Endless scenes playing as if screens from a theatre were filling the spaces all around her, in every direction. She began to float amongst them, spinning to see myriad wonders, bewildered at the images that she was witnessing.

"What is this?" she asked. "What are all of these scenes?"

"Observe," God instructed her, "and they will become familiar."

And familiar they became. The scenes were from her life. Everything that had ever happened. Everything she had ever gone though. Everything she had ever experienced. It was all there. It was marvelous. Seeing her own life all over again. What a wonder. What a gift.

"My life," she cried out. "This is my life. All the people. The places. The experiences. Everything that has ever happened to me." She took it all in and then said it again, but slowly this time, "My life."

"Your life," proclaimed God. "Yes, this is your life. This life. The beautiful life that you chose for yourself. The life that you chose for me. And no, my child, not everything that has ever happened *to* you. It is everything that has ever happened *for* you."

She continued to float amongst the endless scenes. Remembering. Watching again the life she had been living for so many years. Some scenes she remembered well. Some took her a while to recall. And some she did not recognize at all. Some scenes were displayed in bright, vibrant colors. Some were shadowed in darkness. The whole of her life. It was all there before her.

God gave her all the time she needed as time seemed to no longer exist in the world of light. Some scenes she watched again and again, reliving the joy they had brought to her. And some she struggled to witness again, for they brought such great suffering to her life. So much beauty. So much pain. So much bliss and so much hurt. Her life. Her entire life.

And some scenes she realized had never happened. These were the scenes where there was almost no light.

And it came to her. She remembered. "My life," she said, "I chose all of this, didn't I? My God, I was here with you, and I chose all of this."

"No, my child," a long pause. "We did. We chose all of this. Together. You and I. We chose this life for you, together."

"Together," she remembered. "Yes, we chose this life, together." And again, she began to weep. God could see that she was unable to speak, so God would speak for her.

"You came to me as a perfect beautiful soul, and you asked me for life. I granted you that gift, my child. I allowed you to live. But first we were here, in this place. In our place. In the world of light. And in this place, I asked a promise of you. I asked you to serve a purpose with your life. And for that purpose, you would have to endure. But I loved you so much I had to grant you free will. I would allow the choices to be yours. And in this place, I showed you these images. I played you these scenes. Some so desirable, and full of joy. You were so eager to experience them. And some so difficult and full of suffering. You shuddered in fear of their possibilities. Every potential experience that would ever unfold in your entire life, right here, before you."

"And you allowed me to decide, didn't you, my God. You left the choice to me, to live a life with the experiences that I chose to endure."

"Yes, I allowed you to decide. I left it all to you," God reminded her. "I allowed you to see these scenes. To see how they would unfold and how they would guide your life and change your soul."

It was all coming back to her. She was remembering more and more of her last meeting with God. She was recalling the promise that she had made. The reason for all of this. The great suffering. And she spoke to God again, "For my purpose. You offered me these experiences of suffering, for my purpose."

"Yes, my child," the great God replied. "For your purpose. It pained me so greatly to see the scenes of suffering that I offered to you, my beautiful being. For I wish you only joy and happiness. But your purpose could never be fulfilled without your growth. For the light can only be visible amongst the darkness. And your beautiful soul can only grow in suffering. You can only mature in the darkness. You can only nurture your soul through the experiences of suffering. And you, you beautiful creature, *you* chose to suffer for my purpose. You chose to suffer for me."

"I chose these hardships for you, my God. I remember now. I remember all of it," she wept through her words as the weight of her memories began to grow. "I remember you pleading with me to be gentle on myself. I remember you wishing me a life of happiness, but I chose to endure. I chose all of this."

"Yes, you light warrior. You chose the darkness. You agreed to fulfill your purpose so greatly that you would carry the weight of the world by suffering the experiences I presented before you, and for that, my child, I, who am God, am so grateful for you." Then God fell silent.

The woman continued to observe the images around her. The suffering. The images that were not so vibrant. The images that portrayed the most difficult times that had scarred her soul. So many memories that were so familiar. Then she began to focus on the darkest scenes. So dark that they had almost no light. And others that she could not recognize. Images where she saw her older self. "And these, my God?" she asked about, "what of these?"

"The darkness. The scenes of little light," God explained. "Those are of your greatest suffering. You chose those. You, my innocent child. You asked me to place these experiences in your life. For even though they would cause you the greatest of suffering, you knew they would build in you the greatest strength. They would bring your soul closer to me."

"But you forbade me, my God, didn't you?" she asked. "You would not grant me these lessons."

"No, my child, I would not allow you to endure these experiences," God spoke with love. "For as much as I admired your strength for our purpose, I could not allow you to suffer through these. You put your trust in your God, and I knew these experiences would destroy you. These are too much for you to carry. Far too difficult for you to endure. So, I forbade these, because your God will never allow you to endure that which you could not survive."

Tears of gratitude continued to run down her cheeks as she knew that her God was telling the truth. She had always survived. She was still there. And her soul had grown so immensely through all of her struggles. And she asked again of her God, "And these other scenes? The ones I do not recognize? The ones where I appear as my older self."

"These are your future, my child." You chose these experiences of suffering as well, but I have yet to present them to you. They have yet to occur."

"And that is why we are here, isn't it, my God? That is why you have come to me now. I remember. You told me, when we were here together before. You told me you would always be here for me, with me, and that you would not let me fall."

"I will never let you fall," God told her. "No matter how difficult life becomes, I will never let you fall. And as you came close to the edge, I came to bring you back to this place. To remind you of the time when we decided your life, together. And to present you with another choice."

A choice?" she asked. "We will choose again, won't we?

"Yes, sweet child of light," God said, "we will choose again. Before you now are the experiences you still have yet to experience with the days remaining in your life. In the life you still have left to live before you return to me again. To be in our place. All of these experiences, some wonderful and some difficult. All of them here before you. And together, again, we can decide. You can decide. You can change them. Any of them. All of them. If my child wishes to continue with only happiness, then that is what I will bestow upon you for the rest of your days. Gladly, my beautiful child. And if you choose to endure the suffering that is yet to come, then I will stand beside you, always, as you continue to grow and mature. As you continue to fulfill your promise. As you continue toward your great purpose."

"The purpose, my God. My purpose. The reason that I was born into this life. It is far too great. It is necessary for me to return to this place the way I was intended to. And I know what it is."

"Yes, my child," God spoke with affirmation, "you

know your great purpose."

"Love," she said. "My purpose is love."

"Love, my child. Yes. Your purpose is love," God reminded the woman. "And you are the most beautiful love in my world of light."

"But I can love more, my God," she proclaimed loudly. "I can love more for your world. I can love more for you. I can love more for me."

"I love you, my child," God told her. "I love you so much. And I already knew what your answer would be."

"Take me back, my God. I will endure. Take me back to the world into which you granted me life," she said, "and let me continue. I will love with all my heart until I return home to love here, in the world of light, with you."

the fire

There was once a man who walked to every corner of earth seeking an answer to his life. He felt like all of the other men of the world. No different. No more special than those who came before him or those who would come long after he was gone. All the same. The man lived an honorable life, always attempting to live with good intentions and purpose, but sadly, his life felt unfulfilled. The meaning that men seek to guide their lives was never there. Nothing seemed to separate him from all the rest. And his days were just that, days. But he wished to have more than just days, more than just watching the sands fall from the hourglass of his life without the meaning he yearned for. So he continued to walk.

Like many others in the world, he doubted himself. Tremendous doubt was always there. It was so difficult to not doubt. After all, what was to separate him from the others? What was to give him purpose other than his own thoughts? And this was not enough for the man. He knew there was something greater. But what?

And how?

Then one night the man found himself alone, as he often was, walking near a small forest. He admired the earth and all of her living wonder. She was always so beautiful to him, and he stood still, breathing in the cool night air. He had been in this forest many times. It was part of his home, and he felt safe here. But now, on this night, he saw the forest for the first time. Truly saw it. The life of it. The life within it. All of it.

The trees began to breathe with him as he filled his chest with air. The ground pressed back at his feet as he took each of his steps. The winds danced through this hair and gently caressed his skin, and he acknowledged it all for the first time—truly embraced it. He looked up at the sky, and rather than see the vast emptiness of space that had always been there before, he saw the universe looking down at him. Smiling. An unavoidable smile from the heavens. The totality of it began to make his heart race. It was beating heavier and heavier in his chest, and he placed his hands over it to connect with his true self.

What was happening? Why was the night coming to life around him, when so many nights before had always been the same? Then, as the forest began to breathe deeper all around him, he had an moment of awakening—a moment when everything around him erupted with life and an immense light consumed him, and all of the anxiety that was racing through him disappeared. The light blinded him momentarily, but he did not need to see, for he could feel. And he began.

"God," the man spoke into the wind.

"Yes, my child. I am here," God replied to the man.

"Am I dying?" the man calmly asked of God.

"No, my child," God told him. "You are not dying. Far from it. You are being born again, into my world. And I need you. I have something for you."

"For me?" wondered the man. "I am so humbled and grateful, my God, that you would need me, a mere man with nothing to offer you."

"So full of doubt. But why, my son?" God spoke. "I created you and you are a part of me. How can you doubt, my son? How can you question?"

"I am sorry, but this is who I have become. A man riddled with doubt. I am a disappointment to my great God, and I cannot be worthy of anything you have come to give me. Please forgive me, my God. I am here to serve, but what can I offer you?"

God could feel the sorrow inside the man. It was disheartening to God, but all too familiar amongst the children of the world. "You do not need to apologize, you only have to receive, my child. Here is what I have to give you."

And God produced a great heart and presented it to the man. A heart that looked as if it were born from a flower. "This is your heart, my child. Your new heart. I created it from my own heart, and I have come to give it to you. You will need it, for I will ask a great feat from you."

"The heart of God!" The man proclaimed with great

wonder as he admired the gift. It was magnificent, and unlike anything he had ever seen before. "Surely, I am not worthy of such a gift, and it should be given to someone else! What can I, a mere man, do with the heart of God?"

"No, my child, the heart of *you*. The real you. The one that has been deep inside there, forever, waiting to come back to serve my world." God presented the heart one more time, and this time the man took it.

"I will never doubt my great God, and I will be humble and accept that which my God has to present to me," the man stated as he accepted the heart from God. "What am I to do now, my God?"

God placed the heart within the man, and the man felt a new sense of purpose that he had never felt before. And God proclaimed, "You will serve, my child. You will serve the world. This heart has always been yours, and you have allowed it to fall into the shadows, where it was cast into the darkest of caves. But now, here in this place, I will ask you to serve. As I asked of my rock long ago, I will ask the same of you. Here you will create. You will create that which no man could ever tear down. And because of your creation the people of the world will come. They will come to find their own hearts, just as you have."

The man was humbled. He could not find words to express his newfound purpose, but he did not need words. He felt the truth. The truth of God's words. He was given a gift from his great God, and he must live with his new purpose. He must create, just as God asked him to do.

Still speechless, the man remained silent as God spoke again. "This gift is forever, just as you are. The power bestowed in this heart can build worlds. It can move mountains. It can shift galaxies. Please, my child, use it as I intend for you. For the power is so great it can also devastate. This heart can destroy and this heart can end the world. But with you, my child, I know this heart will beat with proper purpose."

The man finally managed to speak back to his God, "Yes, my God. I will not let you down. This gift that you have given to me. I will use it as you intend. My purpose is clear. I feel it within. I understand what I am called to do."

"Begin, my child," God said, "proceed to bring out the hearts of many. For many are lost, and you must create to help them find their way. But first, my child, I must prepare you. I must release this heart so that it may be fully yours. And I must ask a small task of you."

"Anything, my God. I stand here, ready to begin my new life. And I will do anything that is asked of me from my great God."

And God had one more gift to offer the man. It was a bag of seeds, each small and round and unlike any the man had ever seen before. "Seeds?" asked the man, "am I to plant these for you?"

"No, my child. You are to plant these for them," God said in reply.

Filled with questions, the man still chose to remain

silent. He would fulfill God's request and trust that it was all for a purpose. He would not ask further questions, he would just accept the seeds and do as he was asked.

"And now, before I leave you, my child, I must take something from you. So, close your eyes, and see with your heart, and remember that you are still alive."

Once again, the man would not dare question God. He merely closed his eyes and felt the pulse of his heart beating within his chest, and a small smile grew across his face. He could feel the earth all around him as it once again began to breathe. He remained with his eyes closed, for he felt something happening. And then a feeling swept over him. A warmth. A sensation of immense heat that rushed over his body, awakening his soul and lifting it into the sky. It should have felt like a painful inferno, destroying all that was around him. But instead, there was only peace. An uplifting peace the warmth had left for him. And he took a deep breath as he opened his eyes and knew he would never be the same again.

God was gone, and the man stood there at the side of the forest with only a handful of seeds. "I will waste no time," he whispered to himself, and he began to dig small holes in the earth. Placing the seeds, one by one, into the earth as God had asked him. Covering them with dirt with loving intention. And when he was finished, he looked all about him to find comfort in the sacred place where God had come to see him. The place where he'd been reborn.

"Here, I will create," he proclaimed to himself. "Just as the rock, here I will build up what no man could ever tear down." Just as God had instructed him. How could he doubt it? With the guidance of his great God, his creation would help fulfill God's purpose. And so he began.

He gathered from the world that which the world had to offer, and on the sacred ground where God had come to visit him, on the hallowed ground where the man had planted God's seeds, the man would create. He worked diligently, by the sweat of his brow. Never asking for anything from anyone in his pursuit. Always trusting it was part of God's plan. The man would create. Days passed, the hourglass sands continued to pour, but for the first time, the man felt that he was pouring the sands. The days were no longer passing with emptiness. And his heart was full with such great purpose and love. The gift given to him by God would be used just as it was intended. To serve the people of the world.

And finally, after years of work, the man's creation was complete. His vision had been born, and the man stood and admired that which he'd created to fulfill the will of the great God. But he felt it still to be incomplete. Something was missing. Something was needed before God's work could be done. So as the man stood before his creation, looking at it in awe, he turned to looking within himself, seeking the answer.

And the answer presented itself with such surety. It was his heart. The heart that God had given to him as a gift. The heart was the answer. He could not keep it inside of his own chest. It would not do the world enough good there. So he reached within and removed his heart, and he placed it in the center of his creation. And that is where it would remain, so that it could reach the hearts of the many who would come to this place, just as God had told him.

And come they did. First it was a few, but soon it was many. And the man cried God's tears as the sands continued to fall, and the people were served. They would gather often, here at the man's creation. There on God's hallowed ground, above the seeds in the earth. They would be free from their chains, and they would experience so much peace, together. They would share, and they would grow. They would learn, and they would teach. They would mature, and they would rise. They would laugh, and they would cry. They would take in, and they would let go. And most importantly, they would love. And they would be loved.

The heart of God would beat, and the frequency would warm all who were there. All were grateful for the man's creation, as they would surrender to the experience of life in this place. The man was filled with joy, for he had never dreamed of living with such a purpose. He was given a gift, and his gift was awakening those who had fallen asleep. His gift was felt through his words, and through his thoughts. Through his actions, and through his intentions. And the world around him was growing brighter, as many around him were growing within their own hearts as well.

It was harmony. Just as God had always intended it to be.

So the man would create more. He would cultivate the place where many could come so that their hearts could be filled. And the sweat on his brow would accumulate, but he would continue with purpose. Knowing he had to share his gift from God with the people of the world. He believed this would continue forever. But nothing in the material world can be forever.

And so it came. The night of darkness. On the night when the moon was full. The night when fire would rain from the sky in a fury the world had never seen before. The ground shook and the earth screamed as the man watched the flames grow and consume his creation. Mighty flames that reached the stars high in the night sky. And the man fell to his knees. Helpless and destroyed, the man reached his hands forward toward his creation. The fire was taking it from him as the ashes were falling over him like snow falls in the winter. He could do nothing but cry and feel the tears rushing down his face as his creation disappeared from the world. The creation he built to fulfill the will of his great God. It burned until it was gone, taking the heart away with it.

The sands poured, and the time passed once again. His creation burned down to nothing more than ashes on the ground. The devastation was immense. He could barely look at the sacred ground where his creation had once stood. The place he had built for the people of the world to gather and find each other, a place to find themselves, just as God had wished of him. He walked, just as he had when his journey had begun, through the ashes in the place where God had come to see him. And he wept with his face cradled in his own hands. And it happened again. The earth began to breathe with him. The trees came to life and the sky looked down upon the man, as God once again came to be in this place with him.

"God," the man said with great sorrow in his voice. "I have failed you. I was never worthy of such a gift."

"My child," God replied with love, "why do you say that? Why has doubt returned to you?"

"The heart, my God. Your heart," he said slowly, "my heart. And all that came with it. I placed it inside my creation so that the world could receive your love in this great place. And now it is gone. The fire came and destroyed my creation, and it had my heart inside." The man felt so apologetic as he struggled to find the words to speak to his great God.

"The creation?" asked God. "My child, you have forgotten again. The creation was never the gift to the world."

"But you told me, my God, 'Create that which no man will ever tear down.' And I created this place so that many would gather here and their hearts would be filled. And I believed that my God would protect it. My God would keep that which is sacred to the people of the world. And now it is gone. The fire fell from the sky and took it away from us. Reduced to ashes.

Burning my heart with destruction in its flames. So I have failed."

God allowed the man a moment to absorb all that was around him. The silence was deafening. Until God finally spoke with empathy, "My child, it was I who sent the fire to rain from the sky. It was I who reduced the creation to ashes."

"You?!" the man shouted. "But why? Why! My God! I am sorry to rise before you, but I do not understand. Why would my God do this to me? Why would he take this away?"

"Because, my child," said God, "this was never the gift." And again there was a long silence before God spoke again. "Remember, my child, why I came to you. Remember what it is that I said to you, before, here in this sacred place."

"Create what no man could tear down," answered the man. "You asked me to create. With the gift that you gave to me. The gift that was destroyed in the flames."

"Yes, I asked you to create. And that is exactly what you did. And what else did I ask of you, my child?" God asked.

"You asked me to plant the seeds."

"Yes, I asked you to plant the seeds. And that is what you did. You planted the seeds of a flower that can only bloom in the ashes of great fire. A flower that can only grow when the ground has been completely desecrated. A flower that I use to create the hearts of God, that belong to people of the world."

The man raised his head with tears in his eyes. The truth was settling upon him. He realized this was the way it was meant to be. The fire had always been a part of the plan.

"Look around you, my child," God instructed of the man. "Look at the wonder that has been brought to my world."

And the man turned around in the ashes, and saw the many flowers in bloom. Glorious. Marvelous. He could only continue to turn in wonder as he admired all of their beauty. "So many flowers," he cried.

"Yes, so many flowers. One for each of the souls that grew in this place."

"I understand, now, my God," the man spoke softly, "I understand the gift and what you asked me to create. I understand why you came to me, and I understand now why you left."

"The fire, my child," said God.

"The fire," returned the man. "When you left me, here in this place, I stood with my eyes closed and I felt your warmth. That was your fire."

"Yes, my child, that was my fire. The fire that was necessary to burn it all away. Remember I told you that I must take something from you before I left you in this place. I took the doubt from you. You shed it in this place. The doubt and the fear. That which has been keeping you from sharing your gift with the world. It fell from within you onto the ground of this place, and my fire rained down upon you to reduce it to ashes, where it could no longer confine you. The fire cleansed you, my child, so that you could live for your purpose."

The man cried before God, hearing the truth. Trusting in his words, and breathing in faith. "The fire that cleansed me and allowed me to live. Then the great fire you sent that consumed this place. That was for a cleansing, too, wasn't it?"

"It was, my child," God continued with compassion, "You gathered my people here, in this place. And with them they brought their sorrows. They brought their doubts and their fears. And in the place that you created, they shed these things from within themselves. They shed these things and they left them here, on this sacred ground, where you planted the seeds. They prepared themselves to receive my heart. And when my children had grown enough, and I knew they were ready, I rained down the fire, just as I had always intended to do. I rained down the fire to burn their sorrows. To reduce them to ashes where they would never keep the light from my children again. In the ashes their flowers grew, and I will place my heart within each flower, and present each as a gift to all who came to this place."

The man was silent a moment, finding it difficult to speak. It was all real. It was all as it was intended to be. "Thank you, my God, for giving me such a great purpose. Thank you for this gift."

"It was you, my child. You used your gift to prepare the people for their great feat. And it is I, your God, who is grateful to you." God comforted the man. "And the gift could never be destroyed. No flames could ever destroy the heart of the world that belongs inside your chest. You see—" God raised the heart from the ashes and presented it once again to the man.

"My heart, it is still here. Beating louder and more beautifully than ever before."

"Of course, my child. Your heart is far too powerful for any fire to ever destroy. Now do you see? Do you see what you have created? What I asked you to create, here in this place. That which is so great that no man could ever tear it down?"

"Love, my God," replied the man slowly, sure of his answer. "I have created love."

"Yes, my child. You have created love. My love. It's for the people of the world so that they may now find the hearts that are their own gifts. Together, you can save my world."

To you, whom this was written for, never forget who you really are. Never forget what you are capable of. And never forget what you were born into this life to do.

about the author

Amar Abro is the author of Elephant Brain and the co-founder of Elephant Studios, a center for wellness and meditation practice. He has spent the better half of his life traveling the world, gaining the experiences that have become the source of inspiration behind his writing and his practice. He says that his experiences and connections with the people of the world have "allowed God to speak through me and my writing." He wrote this book with the hope of changing the world . . . if even for just one person.

Lightning Source UK Ltd.
Milton Keynes UK
UKHW010430160223
417042UK00010B/1425